LONG JOAN SILVER

A full-length comedy by
Arthur M. Jolly

Based on the novel *Treasure Island* by
Robert Louis Stevenson

www.youthplays.com
info@youthplays.com
424-703-5315

 ISBN 978-1-62088-205-4.

COPYRIGHT RULES TO REMEMBER

1. To produce this play, you must receive prior written permission from YouthPLAYS and pay the required royalty.

2. You must pay a royalty each time the play is performed in the presence of audience members outside of the cast and crew. Royalties are due whether or not admission is charged, whether or not the play is presented for profit, for charity or for educational purposes, or whether or not anyone associated with the production is being paid.

3. No changes, including cuts or additions, are permitted to the script without written prior permission from YouthPLAYS.

4. Do not copy this book or any part of it without written permission from YouthPLAYS.

5. Credit to the author and YouthPLAYS is required on all programs and other promotional items associated with this play's performance.

When you pay royalties, you are recognizing the hard work that went into creating the play and making a statement that a play is something of value. We think this is important, and we hope that everyone will do the right thing, thus allowing playwrights to generate income and continue to create wonderful new works for the stage.

Plays are owned by the playwrights who wrote them. Violating a playwright's copyright is a very serious matter and violates both United States and international copyright law. Infringement is punishable by actual damages and attorneys' fees, statutory damages of up to $150,000 per incident, and even possible criminal sanctions. **Infringement is theft. Don't do it.**

Have a question about copyright? Please contact us by email at info@youthplays.com or by phone at 424-703-5315. When in doubt, please ask.

CAST OF CHARACTERS

Female Roles:

SALLY BONES, a drunken pirate captain, down on her luck.

MRS. HAWKINS, an overprotective mother.

BLIND PEW, a sightless beggarwoman.

LONG JOAN SILVER, a cunning and duplicitous pirate woman - charismatic.

MRS. SITWELL, sarcastic and snappy servant.

MISS BEAN, cheerful and compliant servant.

JEN GUNN, an utterly mad woman, isolated for years.

The Pirates:

ISRAEL HANDS, the most evil of the pirate women.

JACQUOTTE DELCHARGE, scary French woman.

MARY READE, tempestuous.

ANNE BONNEY, ruthless.

TESS MORGAN, dumb as a bag of rope.

MARIA LINDSEY, brave—perhaps reckless.

MARY "CRICKET" CRICHETT, petite and feisty.

LIZ PATRICKSON, rough and ready Irish lass.

Male Roles:

JIM HAWKINS, a 12-year-old boy.

SQUIRE TRELAWNEY, upper class, overprivileged dandy.

DR. LIVESEY, a country doctor.

CAPTAIN SMOLLETT, a stiff, principled, but old-fashioned sea captain.

FIRST MATE ALAN ARROW, sadistic.

BOSUN ABRAHAM GRAY, loyal and brave.

TOM REDRUTH, a ship's carpenter who speaks in Sussex dialect. Incomprehensible.

Inn Patrons:

FARMER GILES, bluff and simple.

DOUG THE UNDERTAKER, sallow and creepy.

BONES THE BUTCHER, could bench press a bull.

PETER THE PORTER, quiet—only one word (but gets a laugh.)

Roles for Male or Female:

THE PARROT, a recorded sound effect, or an off stage voice performer.

Merchants:

MEAT PIE SELLER

MERCHANT OF THINGS

FRUIT DEALER

INN PATRONS, DOCKSIDE SAILORS.

Small Cast

Doubles and triples are possible, some roles can combine.

Large Cast

The four bar patrons become seven. Pirates divide roles. Playwright assistance with combining or dividing roles happily given. Occasions when the exact number of pirates is mentioned in the dialogue can of course be changed to suit.

A NOTE ON CASTING

The play is about traditional societal roles and restrictions based on class, privilege and gender. While a particular character may be played by an actor of either gender, that should not change the gender of the character (i.e. if a character is male, the role should be played as male, regardless of the actor's gender). It is anticipated that the role of Jim will typically be played by a girl.

TIME

1756, the Golden Age of Piracy.

SETTING

ACT I
Scene 1—The Admiral Benbow Inn.
Scene 2—A foggy country lane.
Scene 3—The Hispaniola.
Scene 4—Dockside in Bristol.
Scene 5—The Hispaniola.
Scene 6—The Hispaniola.
Scene 7—The captain's cabin.

ACT II
Scene 1—The stockade.
Scene 2—The island.
Scene 3—The Hispaniola.
Scene 4—The island.
Scene 5—The stockade.
Scene 6—The island shoreline.

SET DESIGN

Sets can be simple or elaborate—or a combination, where even numbered scenes play in front of a curtain or scrim while the major set pieces (odd numbered scenes) are set/struck.

In the second act, it may be preferable to set Scene 3 on a separate, partial Hispaniola set (maybe the bow & jib), in front of the curtain, and leave the Stockade set in place.

The descriptions in the text are only what the playwright assumed for basic staging—considerable flexibility is expected in adjusting the action given the constraints of creating a pirate ship on stage, etc.

A NOTE ON WEAPONRY

There's no way to stage a version of *Treasure Island* without pistols, muskets and swords; but it is hoped by this playwright that all gunfire—in particular the assault on the stockade with its close quarters—be presented by sound effects and brilliant acting. The dangers (not to mention the expense) of blank-firing period weapons should not be underestimated.

Long Joan Silver received a staged reading on June 2nd, 2013 at Pacific Resident Theatre (Los Angeles, California).

Cast was as follows:

SALLY BONES	Dalia Vosylius
JIM HAWKINS	Kate Huffman
MRS. HAWKINS	Rita Obermeyer
SQUIRE TRELAWNEY	Michael Rothhaar
DR. LIVESEY	Kim Estes
FARMER GILES	Ed Levy
DOUG THE UNDERTAKER	John Siskel
BONES THE BUTCHER	Dan Cole
PETER THE PORTER	Danielle Ozymandias
BLIND PEW	Jeni Bartiromo
ISRAEL HANDS	Laura Crow
JACQUOTTE DELCHARGE	Tara Donovan
MARY READE	Nikki McCauley
ANNE BONNEY	Christy Buchholz
TESS MORGAN	Lia Kozatch
MARIA LINDSEY	Laura Crow
MARY "CRICKET" CRICHETT	Jeni Bartiromo
LIZ PATRICKSON	Whitton Frank
MRS. SITWELL	Christy Buchholz
MISS BEAN	Whitton Frank
LONG JOAN SILVER	Sarah Zinser
THE PARROT	Ed Levy
CAPTAIN SMOLLETT	Bill Jones
FIRST MATE ALAN ARROW	John Siscel
BOSUN ABRAHAM GRAY	Ed Levy
TOM REDRUTH	Dan Cole
JEN GUNN	Nikki McCauley

ACT I

SCENE 1

(Our play starts in the Admiral Benbow Inn, a quiet country pub in Black Hill Cove, in England's north country. There are two entrances – one ostensibly to the upstairs rooms, [Side] the other to the outside [Front Door] and a sign that reads: Room and Board – tuppence. Room and Bed – fourpence. CAPTAIN SALLY BONES sprawls across a table, a mug of grog in her hand.)

SALLY: *(Music is appended. Sings:)* Fifteen men on a dead man's chest, yo ho ho and a bottle of rum,
Drink and the devil had done for the rest, yo *heave* ho...and a bottle of uh...something.

(She drinks:)

Wi' only one man left alive, yo ho ho and a bottle of rum,
What put to sea wi' seventy-five,
Yo *heave* ho and a bottle of rum!
'Twas a cutlass swipe or an ounce of lead,
Or a yawin' hole in a battered head,
And the scuppers ran with a rotting red.
There they lay, under sodden skies,
Their lookouts fixed on paradise,
Their souls bound just contrarywise –
Yo *heave* ho and a bottle of...

(She thinks:)

Rum!

(She leaps up.)

SALLY: Cabin boy – avast! Fetch more rum, me mug's as dry as the bones of me old shipmate, Cap'n Flint. Buried with a secret, Flint was. Fill me mug, boy, and we'll drink to Cap'n Flint's bones, and a secret never found out!

(JIM HAWKINS enters, as though pushed.)

JIM: *(To the unseen pusher behind him:)* Mum!

SALLY: There ye are! More rum, sprog.

JIM: Maybe you've had enough, ma'am.

MRS. HAWKINS: *(Off:)* Don't forget the money!

JIM: And you...uh...the shillings you gave my mother...you've drunk them. And then some.

SALLY: *(Threatening with the sword:)* Is it me credit you're worried about, lad?

JIM: More your cutlass! *(Beat.)* My mother had some concerns in that direction.

SALLY: A fine woman, wi' scarcely a hair on her chin that ain't proper.

(She fishes a gold coin from her purse.)

There ye are—a gold doubloon. I'll reckon I can drink on that a few more nights, aye?

(Jim brings a bottle over.)

JIM: A week at least, even at the amount you...that'll do nicely.

(Sally offers the coin – but withdraws it at the last second.)

SALLY: Have you seen her?

JIM: No Ma'am. I've been watching careful, like you said.

SALLY: A one-legged seafarin' woman...and her evil shipmates, all women. Scraggly, mangy women. She-devils of the sea!

JIM: I've been looking, Mistress Bones, lookin' out my window with a spyglass every chance I get, looking for women, hoping ever so much to see one. No women. Not one.

(MRS. HAWKINS enters.)

MRS. HAWKINS: You've been doing *what*?

JIM: Not like that, mum! I was only watching on behalf of Sally Bones! She's afeared of a one-legged woman and her cutthroat crew!

MRS. HAWKINS: *(Praying:)* Lord, in your mercy, please strike my son blind for his sinful ways. Thank you.

SALLY: Quit jabberin'! The lad watches for me on my orders as captain of this ship!

MRS. HAWKINS: This is my pub, Cap'n Bones.

SALLY: Captain of this pub!

MRS. HAWKINS: A woman posin' as captain—it's not natural.

SALLY: And who runs this pub?

MRS. HAWKINS: Don't change the subject. Going to sea...is that any place for a woman?

SALLY: *(Simply:)* It be every place for a woman.

MRS. HAWKINS: That's as may be, but I'll thank you to keep your wild sea yarns to yourself. You're giving the boy ideas.

JIM: I think it would be a fine adventure.

MRS. HAWKINS: Exactly! No son of mine will ever set foot on a ship—and I'll be putting a parental control on that spyglass, too.

JIM: Mum!

SALLY: Lad—just keep a weather eye out for that evil creature and her horde. I'll take me grog to go.

(She slams the coin down on the table, grabs the bottle and exits to the rooms. A pause.)

MRS. HAWKINS: She's gone.

(From every possible hiding place various PATRONS emerge, behind the bar, inside barrels, behind curtains, under tables...the more the funnier. Among them are DR. LIVESEY, SQUIRE TRELAWNEY, FARMER GILES, DOUG THE UNDERTAKER, BONES THE BUTCHER, PETER THE PORTER and others.)

SQUIRE TRELAWNEY: She's gone—truly?

MRS. HAWKINS: Aye.

DR. LIVESEY: What an unpleasant creature. Such language!

SQUIRE TRELAWNEY: Disgusting. Drinking rum in the middle of the day. *(To Jim:)* Jim lad—a glass of rum.

JIM: Aye aye, Squire.

SQUIRE TRELAWNEY: Yes. It's "Yes, Squire" not "Aye aye"—you're not a sailor.

JIM: I wish I were. Sailing on the seven seas, fighting with pirates, battling a gale round the Cape.

SQUIRE TRELAWNEY: Teeth rotting of scurvy and body shaking from yellowjack, like as not. You'll not catch me ploughing the ocean waves, not for all the tea in China.

FARMER GILES: Can't do that anyhows—the horses would sink.

MRS. HAWKINS: We must do something. She's driving away all my business!

BONES THE BUTCHER: Who wants to drink where you might get hit with a cutlass?

DOUG THE UNDERTAKER: And those songs she sings—they give me nightmares!

DR. LIVESEY: There's only one thing for it. We must convince her to give up the demon drink, and turn her into a decent woman.

DOUG THE UNDERTAKER: Aye! Then perhaps she will learn her place—doing laundry and so forth.

BONES THE BUTCHER: Aye—we stop her drinking first thing!

MRS. HAWKINS: Now Gentlemen, let's not be hasty—mayhap there's a way I could keep your business, and still get her money as well... She drinks almost as much as the rest of you put together, 'cepting the Squire.

SQUIRE TRELAWNEY: Thank you m'dear—but it's her or us.

MRS. HAWKINS: I'm just a poor widow trying to keep a roof over her head...

SQUIRE TRELAWNEY: There's nothing for it—we'll have to drink more to make up the loss.

DR. LIVESEY: A creditable plan.

SQUIRE TRELAWNEY: Rum for everyone!

PATRONS: Huzzah!

MRS. HAWKINS: You're a fine man, Squire, and ready to do your part for the common good.

SQUIRE TRELAWNEY: The question is—how do we break this woman of her fiendish addiction?

DR. LIVESEY: Jim, lad—you've heard her yarns, her wild tales of pirates, of sea-battles...is there nowt she's afraid of?

JIM: Only a one-legged woman, Doctor. A sea-faring woman, like herself. She lives in mortal peril of her.

DR. LIVESEY: I have an idea. Mrs. Hawkins—I must see your wardrobe.

MRS. HAWKINS: Doctor! I am a widow, not a fallen woman!

DR. LIVESEY: *(Dry:)* You have nothing to fear on that account. Show me to your wardrobe.

(Dr. Livesy and Mrs. Hawkins exit at the side door. A HAMMERING on the front door.)

JIM: Who is out there?

BLIND PEW: (*Off:***)** 'Tis I—Blind Pew! A poor beggarwoman, who has lost the precious sight of her eyes— All heaven bless you and keep you from such a fate yourself.

(Jim opens the front door, and BLIND PEW enters, tapping her way with her staff. Her eyes are wrapped with a crusty, stained bandage. Peter the Porter closes the door behind her.)

Can any kind soul tell me where I may be?

JIM: You are at the Admiral Benbow Inn, Black Hill Cove.

BLIND PEW: A voice! A young voice. Will you give me your hand, my kind young friend, and lead me in?

(Jim offers his hand, and Pew grabs his arm, twisting it.)

Where is she?

JIM: Ow! Let go—you're hurting me!

BLIND PEW: I can hurt you more! Take me to the woman that calls herself Capt'n Sally Bones or I'll twist yer arm clean from yer socket, I will!

SQUIRE TRELAWNEY: I say—let him go!

(A pause.)

BLIND PEW: Is there someone else here?

SQUIRE TRELAWNEY: Yes, there is!

FARMER GILES: More than one.

DOUG THE UNDERTAKER: There's a whole bunch of us.

BONES THE BUTCHER: I'm here, but don't tell my wife.

(The other Patrons ad-lib: "Aye," "Me too," "I'm here, Huckleberry," etc.)

BLIND PEW: Oh. *(To Jim:)* I thought you was alone. *(Beat.)* I'll come back later.

(She turns and runs into the door. Wham. A beat. Peter opens the door for her.)

PETER THE PORTER: Sorry.

(Blind Pew staggers out. Sally Bones enters from the side door.)

SALLY: That voice! I heard me a voice I ain't heard in a crow's age... and yet not long enough!

SQUIRE TRELAWNEY: She's gone. A blind beggarwoman...Pew!

BONES THE BUTCHER: *(Waving the air around himself:)* Sorry—that was me.

SALLY: They've found me. They've tracked me down! Boy! Fetch me a mug of grog!

JIM: The doctor said—

SALLY: Curses on that sawbones! 'Tis rum I need, lad!

(Dr. Livesy enters – wearing a dress and hopping on one leg.)

DR. LIVESEY: *(Falsetto:)* Oh, I've been sailing up and down the ocean! Sally Bones, 'tis I—come to warn you of the demon drink!

(Sally freezes – too afraid to turn around.)

SALLY: Jim lad—speak to me truly—what stands behind me?

JIM: A fearsome sight, Mistress Bones—I do not lie.

SALLY: A one-legged woman?

JIM: In a manner of...I see only one leg, Mistress.

SALLY: A sea-faring woman, though—truly?

JIM: I have never seen such a one as her on land.

DR. LIVESEY: *(Falsetto:)* Aye aye wi' a mainbrace, and hoist up the bowsprit, arrh, arrh—shiver me timbers wi' a marlinspike. Shun the demon drink, says I!

FARMER GILES: Or at least go to some other pub.

(Sally clutches her heart...and collapses.)

JIM: She fainted!

(Dr. Livesy checks her pulse.)

DR. LIVESEY: 'Tis a stroke!

DOUG THE UNDERTAKER: Fetch a doctor!

DR. LIVESEY: I am the doctor!

SQUIRE TRELAWNEY: Fetch a doctor who isn't wearing a dress!

DR. LIVESEY: I can still doctor, Squire Trelawney, for all my attire may be unconventional!

FARMER GILES: 's not proper, a woman in the medical profession!

DR. LIVESEY: I'm not a woman!

BONES THE BUTCHER: By his outfit, sir, a man is known.

SQUIRE TRELAWNEY: Well said—put on your breeches this instant!

JIM: I think she's dying.

SQUIRE TRELAWNEY: And quick, hang you—this woman's dying!

JIM: Please hurry, Doctor.

SALLY: A glass of rum. Just a tot.

DR. LIVESEY: A tot of rum won't kill you, Sally Bones, but if you take one you'll take another and another, and I stake my wig if you don't break off short, you'll die—do you understand that? Die.

(Dr. Livesy exits at the side door.)

SALLY: You heard the doctor—a tot won't kill me.

(Dr. Livesy pops back in again.)

DR. LIVESEY: Sally—listen to me now—the name of rum for you is death!

(He exits.)

SALLY: Quick, Jim, a glass of death!

FARMER GILES: 'tain't right, a woman hogging all the rum.

DOUG THE UNDERTAKER: We must cure you of this terrible affliction.

SALLY: I'm dying!

SQUIRE TRELAWNEY: Yes, but that doesn't mean you can drink all the rum first.

SALLY: One last glass before I hoist me anchor for a distant shore.

SQUIRE TRELAWNEY: Well...one.

(The Squire starts to proffer his mug – catches himself. Eyes it. To Jim:)

Got anything smaller?

(Jim indicates: behind the bar. As Squire Trelawney goes to fetch the tiniest mug you've ever seen, Sally clutches Jim's arm:)

SALLY: Jim, lad – me heart – it's done for.

JIM: Your heart!

SALLY: Look in me chest.

JIM: For your heart?

SALLY: No, me heart's not in me chest.

JIM: Yes it is.

SALLY: No, it ain't!

JIM: I can check with the doctor, but I'm pretty sure it is.

SALLY: Look in me chest, lad! Reach in the lining and find me map!

(Jim reaches into her bodice – Mrs. Hawkins enters.)

MRS. HAWKINS: What are you doing, Jim!

JIM: She asked me to!

MRS. HAWKINS: *(Praying:)* Oh Lord, please bless my son with the plague so that his dirty hands fall off and he won't be tempted, amen.

PATRONS: Amen.

SQUIRE TRELAWNEY: God bless us, every one!

SALLY: Not my bodice, my sea chest!

JIM: I'm so sorry—I honestly thought you meant...

(He gestures. Mrs. Hawkins clips him upside the head.)

MRS. HAWKINS: That's for what you was thinking.

SALLY: Inside me sea chest!

JIM: What's inside your sea chest?

SALLY: Treasure, lad. A fortune in treasure!

(A beat.)

SQUIRE TRELAWNEY: Out! Everyone out. Get out! This woman needs air! Give her some room!

(All the Patrons exit the front door.)

MRS. HAWKINS: I'll fetch the Doctor!

SQUIRE TRELAWNEY: And his breeches!

(Mrs. Hawkins exits at the side as the Squire kneels down and offers Sally his glass of rum.)

Treasure, did you say?

SALLY: Captain Flint's treasure—a fortune in gold we had, and we buried it on a deserted isle... And it's all in me sea chest!

SQUIRE TRELAWNEY: Don't be silly, an island would never fit!

SALLY: A map. There's a map in it.

SQUIRE TRELAWNEY: Well strike me blue and call me Dora.

JIM: Captain Flint's great secret...was a map?

SALLY: That weren't Flint's secret—that's long buried.

SQUIRE TRELAWNEY: Captain Flint—who terrorized all England with his wicked ways? He left buried treasure?

SALLY: That's why they're after me. They've come for the map.

JIM: Who's after you?

SQUIRE TRELAWNEY: When you say a fortune, do you have an approximate value? What kind of pound sterling amount are we talking?

SALLY: Jim—you've always been a good lad—kept a fair lookout for me old shipmates for me. I 'preciate it, I do, and you can lay to that.

SQUIRE TRELAWNEY: Because a fortune for yourself, or some such minimum-wage earning welfare leech, is hardly going to keep me in boots for a month.

SALLY: Don't let that scurvy crew get their blood-smirched hands upon it.

JIM: I won't, Cap'n.

SQUIRE TRELAWNEY: Whereas what someone of my station might consider a fortune, I doubt you could conceive of such a sum.

SALLY: Seven hundred thousand pounds, Squire, in gold and precious jewels, taken from the Spanish by Captain Flint's own hand. Flint burned a dozen galleons to get it, and sent two hundred Spanish souls to a watery grave.

SQUIRE TRELAWNEY: Oh, it makes one proud to be British. Seven hundred thousand, you say?

SALLY: Is that fortune enough for you?

SQUIRE TRELAWNEY: For good King George and half the members of Parliament, I should imagine. With that kind of money, one could buy an election! Quick now, where do I find this map?

SALLY: It's the boy I'm giving it to.

JIM: What?

SQUIRE TRELAWNEY: Him? What does he know about money—he's as poor as a widow's son. *(To Jim:)* No offense to your father, Jim, but let's face it—the man's dead. Dead, dead, dead. Moldering in the ground, being eaten by worms, and...what's that kind of fly that lays its eggs in rotting meat? You know the ones, little white maggots wriggling everywhere. Those. *(Beat.)* Sorry, I just realized that was tactless... *(To Sally:)* ...what with you dying and all. Got that to look forward to, I s'pose. My bad. *(Beat.)* Tragic, in a way, for the lad—but they get over it at that age. It was weeks ago.

SALLY: Jim! I want you to have it, lad! Take the map. Get yerself aboard a ship, kill the captain, kill the crew, and sail it...to Treasure Island!

JIM: I can't do that!

SALLY: Sure you can—just pull the ropes and turn the wheel in the direction you want to go.

JIM: I could never kill a fellow human being.

SALLY: Once you have that map...you won't have no say in the matter. They're coming for it.

JIM: I won't kill.

SALLY: You have a good heart. Wish I did.

(She dies. Mrs. Hawkins and Dr. Livesy enter.)

SQUIRE TRELAWNEY: You're too late, Doctor. I'm afraid she has expired.

DR. LIVESEY: I warned her that rum would be the death of her!

SQUIRE TRELAWNEY: I think it was a heart attack seeing you in a dress. I know it gave me a fair turn.

DR. LIVESEY: Well, I'm putting "rum" on the death certificate, and none the wiser.

(A creepy TAPPING on the front door.)

BLIND PEW: *(Off:)* Are ye in there, Captain Bones?!

JIM: I'm still not alone!

BLIND PEW: *(Off:)* Neither am I!

(A HAMMERING at the walls of the pub, the windows – voices of the Pirates yelling.)

MRS. HAWKINS: Lord, they'll murder us in our beds!

DR. LIVESEY: There's no time for that Mrs. Hawkins—we must flee!

SQUIRE TRELAWNEY: Mrs. Hawkins—quick—Sally Bones' sea chest!

MRS. HAWKINS: Don't be ridiculous, Squire—we'll never fit in that!

SQUIRE TRELAWNEY: Not to hide—there's a map in it—we must find it!

(The four of them exit out the side as a crew of ragged female pirates enter – including Blind Pew, ISRAEL HANDS,

JACQUOTTE DELCHARGE, MARY READE, ANNE BONNEY, TESS MORGAN, MARIA LINDSEY, MARY "CRICKET" CRICHETT and LIZ PATRICKSON. They are real pirates, not Halloween-style "girly" pirates. They'll kill you.)

BLIND PEW: She's here! I can smell that traitorous dog! You can't hide from me, Sally Bones—be you ne'er so well hid, I'll find ya if I have to scrape the far corners of the earth for ya!

(Blind Pew trips over Sally's dead body – touches it – works her way up – feels its face.)

I found her!

MARIA LINDSEY: Aye, we uh...we know. We didn't want to say anything.

BLIND PEW: She'm be dead, ain't she.

MARY READE: That she be. And lucky for it.

JACQUOTTE DELCHARGE: Not so lucky for us. She would've told us where she hid ze map.

ISRAEL HANDS: Eventually.

TESS MORGAN: I wish she were alive, so's I could kill 'er again, for being...dead. Already.

CRICKET: That thing ye be doing with your mouth right now? Stop it.

BLIND PEW: It's in her sea chest. I heard her tell that boy, clear as a glass bell.

MARIA LINDSEY: Find it! Find the sea chest!

BLIND PEW: Find the chest and ya find the map—find the map and ya find the island—find the island...and ya find the treasure!

ANNE BONNEY: Tear this place apart!

(The pirates cheer and start ransacking. Lights out.)

SCENE 2

(A country lane near the Inn. Dark, misty. Dr. Livesy helps a limping Squire Trelawney on. Behind them Mrs. Hawkins and Jim enter, dragging a heavy sea chest.)

SQUIRE TRELAWNEY: I think we ditched them.

DR. LIVESEY: Probably by falling in that ditch.

SQUIRE TRELAWNEY: That was a strategic covering maneuver. I cleverly led us into a muddy ditch in the dark to avoid discovery.

DR. LIVESEY: And twisted your ankle.

MRS. HAWKINS: What will become of us?

SQUIRE TRELAWNEY: Don't fret yourself, Mrs. Hawkins—in this chest lies a salve for that worried brow.

MRS. HAWKINS: Botox?

SQUIRE TRELAWNEY: In this chest— *(To Mrs. Hawkins:)* Shhh!

(Sounds of BANGING and CLATTERING in the distance—possibly stage hands changing scenery behind the curtain or scrim, but who writes to cover those sounds?)

MRS. HAWKINS: They're tearing the Admiral Benbow apart. My home, my livelihood gone.

SQUIRE TRELAWNEY: Aye—they're looking for this chest.

DR. LIVESEY: Or turning the inn into a boat.

SQUIRE TRELAWNEY: Don't give it away.

DR. LIVESEY: Why is an old sea chest so important to them?

SQUIRE TRELAWNEY: You might well ask.

DR. LIVESEY: I did well ask. Just now—weren't you well listening?

MRS. HAWKINS: Gentlemen! Please, do not fight amongst yourselves! This chest belonged to Cap'n Bones, who paid us in advance...

SQUIRE TRELAWNEY: Did she pay you for the damage her compatriots cause as we speak?

MRS. HAWKINS: I'll take what's coming to me, and not a farthing more.

SQUIRE TRELAWNEY: You say that now...

JIM: My mother's right. Cap'n Bones came by her treasure unlawfully, and evil follows it.

SQUIRE TRELAWNEY: Methinks you will change your mind, Mrs. Hawkins—when you see what this simple sea chest holds!

(The Squire flings it open and pulls out a pair of bloomers.)

MRS. HAWKINS: Ladies unmentionables!

JIM: Are those really...

DR. LIVESEY: Put those away, Squire!

SQUIRE TRELAWNEY: Why—afraid you're going to want to wear them?

DR. LIVESEY: Think of the lad!

JIM: Her legs were in those. Her actual legs...

MRS. HAWKINS: Oh merciful Lord, please bestow my son with the gift of a metastatic ulceration behind his eye so that his brain stops fermenting such wicked thoughts.

JIM: ...with knees and ankles.

SQUIRE TRELAWNEY: Amen.

DR. LIVESEY: As a medical man, I must insist! You are overheating the lad's imagination!

(The Doctor grabs the bloomers from the Squire and puts them back in the chest.)

SQUIRE TRELAWNEY: Not the bloomers, inside this chest there should be...

DR. LIVESEY: Old sea boots.

SQUIRE TRELAWNEY: Old boots? Something's afoot!

DR. LIVESEY: The remains of a scallop—

SQUIRE TRELAWNEY: What, the shell?

DR. LIVESEY: A lead line with no weight on it...

SQUIRE TRELAWNEY: Unfathomable.

DR. LIVESEY: And a broken spyglass.

SQUIRE TRELAWNEY: I don't see how that could work.

DR. LIVESEY: I'll look into it.

SQUIRE TRELAWNEY: It's beyond my scope.

MRS. HAWKINS: Gentlemen! You must focus!

(They bow to the audience.)

SQUIRE TRELAWNEY: Is there no map inside?

DR. LIVESEY: Yes. Absolutely...no map.

SQUIRE TRELAWNEY: With her dying breath, she swore it.

JIM: Let me see.

SQUIRE TRELAWNEY: I think you can trust the doctor, for all his peculiar dressing habits.

DR. LIVESEY: Let it go.

JIM: Look—the lining of the lid—it's been sewn up—but you can see where it was cut open before.

DR. LIVESEY: Good eyes, Jim—both of them! Tear it open!

(Jim rips open the lining to the trunk lid—and pulls out the map.)

JIM: The map...Treasure Island.

SQUIRE TRELAWNEY: We have it. A map that leads to a vasty treasure—

MRS. HAWKINS: An ill-gotten treasure, no doubt, stained with the blood of innocents.

SQUIRE TRELAWNEY: Seven hundred thousand pounds in gold.

MRS. HAWKINS: Blood washes off is what I always say.

JIM: Mum!

MRS. HAWKINS: Seven hundred thousand pounds!

SQUIRE TRELAWNEY: Aye.

DR. LIVESEY: Pirate treasure...

SQUIRE TRELAWNEY: Spanish gold.

DR. LIVESEY: That's what they all *claim*. Any salt sea-pirate will swear blind he's only after Spanish ships, but I'll stake my vest there's British bullion mixed with it, and the lives of our fair sailors on their hands.

SQUIRE TRELAWNEY: My good doctor—

DR. LIVESEY: Would you take the word of a pirate?

SQUIRE TRELAWNEY: DOCTOR LIVESEY! *(More calmly:)* If I may...assuming this treasure is entirely Spanish in origin—

DR. LIVESEY: Quite an assumption, and one ill-fitting rational contemplation—

SQUIRE TRELAWNEY: IF I MAY!... May we assume, purely for hypothetical purposes, that this vasty treasure is indeed Spanish gold. It behooves us, does it not, as English gentlemen, to recover this treasure from where it molders, perhaps to be stolen by thieves or the French—I repeat myself—and see that it regains its rightful place in England...as legitimate spoils of war, to be divided amongst those English gentlemen that so graciously lent their efforts to its noble recovery.

MRS. HAWKINS: Finders keepers, losers weepers, is it?

SQUIRE TRELAWNEY: Mrs. Hawkins, your perspicuity cuts to the heart of the matter. Yes, I propose that in less than a month—a fortnight—within ten days at most, we embark upon a ship to recover this treasure and endow ourselves as rightful owners.

JIM: It's stolen money.

SQUIRE TRELAWNEY: Not after we dig it up. Then it is found money—which is the second best kind.

DR. LIVESEY: What's the best kind of money?

SQUIRE TRELAWNEY: Mine. And given that I will be, by necessity, funding this expedition, I will take the lion's share of the proceeds.

MRS. HAWKINS: She gave it to the boy.

SQUIRE TRELAWNEY: You heard that?

JIM: She has amazing hearing.

SQUIRE TRELAWNEY: Well then, the boy and I shall split—

DR. LIVESEY: I was the attending physician—it is my name you'll need on any legalities—

SQUIRE TRELAWNEY: As I was saying, equal shares. The loot divided in four parts, one for each of us...

MRS. HAWKINS: Ooh, I get some?!

SQUIRE TRELAWNEY: No, my dear, you're a woman, it would not be seemly. But I trust Jim will take care of his aging mother in her dotage from his share.

MRS. HAWKINS: Aging?!

JIM: Mum—a quarter share would be enough for us to live a hundred lives.

SQUIRE TRELAWNEY: Well spoken, m'lad. The fourth share shall be given to the captain, the officers, ship rental reimbursement, wear and tear on sailcloth and sundry supplies.

DR. LIVESEY: So you're not actually funding the entire—

SQUIRE TRELAWNEY: Can you afford a ship? Then button up your petticoats!

JIM: What ship, Squire?

SQUIRE TRELAWNEY: The ship we must hire, Jim. I travel to Bristol on the morrow, to find the stoutest ship that can be rented cheaply, and the saltiest crew that will work for a handshake and a promise. We're going to sea, Jim lad, ploughing the ocean waves!

MRS. HAWKINS: Those poor horses.

DR. LIVESEY: I knew it!

(Lights out.)

SCENE 3

(On board the schooner Hispaniola. The Hispaniola has two playing areas, visually separated although not necessarily on two levels, referred to as the deck and the stern. There are three entrances – two at the deck [the foc'sle hatch to the lower decks, and climbing over the railing onto the ship, presumably from some small boat anchored alongside] and one at the stern, ostensibly leading to the aft cabins. [Stern portal.] At the deck, two servants, MRS. SITWELL and MISS BEAN, struggle to get a large sea chest over the railing.)

MRS. SITWELL: What's he got in here?

MISS BEAN: Everything.

MRS. SITWELL: Feels like it.

(They get the chest balanced on the railing, and climb over onto the deck. It starts to tip back over the edge – they struggle to right it. More comedic byplay as befits [think Laurel and Hardy's The Music Box*] ending up with Mrs. Sitwell pinned under it on the deck.)*

MISS BEAN: Need a hand?

MRS. SITWELL: Nah, that's all right. I'll just stay here for the voyage. *(Beat.)* 'Course I need an 'and, yer great pillock!

(Miss Bean grabs it and heaves...it moves a bit, then thumps back down on Mrs Sitwell again.)

Yer supposed to be liftin' it, not delivering a coup de flippin' grâce!

MISS BEAN: I was lifting it! It's heavy!

MRS. SITWELL: Really? Heavy is it, 'coz I 'adn't noticed. It's on my bleedin' chest!

MISS BEAN: The chest is on your chest? Huh. On your chest...is a chest!

MRS. SITWELL: Get some help, yer daft biddy!

(Miss Bean looks around:)

Take yer time, I'm not going anywhere.

MISS BEAN: There's no one here.

MRS. SITWELL: I can see that!

(BOSUN ABRAHAM GRAY enters from the foc'sle. He looks at the two:)

BOSUN GRAY: Landlubbers.

(He walks past them to the stern and exits.)

MISS BEAN: He called you a lubber.

MRS. SITWELL: Get this off me!

(Bean heaves—they manage tip the chest off her. Squire Trelawney, dressed like an Admiral with extra gold frogging, enters from the stern portal.)

SQUIRE TRELAWNEY: There you are! Don't loll about.

MRS. SITWELL: Where do you want it, Squire?

SQUIRE TRELAWNEY: My cabin—through the hatch, down a couple of ladders, all the way to the back along a narrow gangway, past the Doctor's cabin, up the aft ladder before you reach the herpetarium beyond the infirmary on the lower deck after you've gone past the stuffed moose head next to the live moose head, second door on the right past the spiky bit, and mind the vase, the bunkside table's a trifle wobbly.

(A beat.)

MRS. SITWELL: Right you are, guvnor. *(To Bean:)* You heard the Squire, don't loll about.

(They struggle past with the chest. CAPTAIN SMOLLETT enters from the stern.)

CAPTAIN SMOLLETT: *(As they struggle past him:)* Landlubbers.

SQUIRE TRELAWNEY: Captain Smollett! My servants are here—finally. And what are we waiting for? Eight days and we're still short crew! Isn't there some temp agency you can contact?

CAPTAIN SMOLLETT: My ship, Squire. I'll not have a man aboard her I can't vouch for—especially when I have sealed orders, no heading to steer by, no destination given. It's a dubious voyage when the Captain his-self can't be trusted.

SQUIRE TRELAWNEY: When we are far from shore, you'll know our course.

DR. LIVESEY: *(Off:)* Permission to come aboard!

SQUIRE TRELAWNEY: Dr. Livesy! Permission—

CAPTAIN SMOLLETT: Permission granted! It is my ship, Squire. I give the orders.

SQUIRE TRELAWNEY: It's my voyage, Captain Smollett, and my funds.

(Dr. Livesy and Jim climb over the railing.)

DR. LIVESEY: What a journey! The traffic was unthinkable—horses nose to tail—must've been eight or nine carts trying to get into the city at once.

SQUIRE TRELAWNEY: Well you're here now.

JIM: Look at this ship! Isn't it wonderful!

CAPTAIN SMOLLETT: A fair ship she is, lad. She'll lie a point nearer the wind than a man has a right to expect of his own married wife.

JIM: When do we set sail?

SQUIRE TRELAWNEY: Not yet, more's the pity. She is a sound ship, Hawkins, and well-founded but she lacks a crew.

CAPTAIN SMOLLETT: I have made my feelings plain, Squire—

SQUIRE TRELAWNEY: Luckily for you, I have taken it upon myself to acquire the ship's cook.

CAPTAIN SMOLLETT: A cook?

SQUIRE TRELAWNEY: Absolutely. I may not know seafaring, but when it comes to recognizing a dab hand in the kitchen, I reckon I've eaten my share of hot suppers and then some. The meal I had at the Spyglass Inn last night was so toothsome, I hired the cook on the spot.

CAPTAIN SMOLLETT: 'Twas not your place.

SQUIRE TRELAWNEY: I reckon her a fine addition to the crew, and the matter is settled.

CAPTAIN SMOLLETT: I said—*(Beat.) Her*?

SQUIRE TRELAWNEY: Aye, Captain—you said you'd take no man aboard you'd not vetted yourself—but nary a thing about a woman. She's a fine cook, and to allay your protestations, she's an old hand before the mast—sailed with Admiral Hawke. Joan! Joan Silver!

(From the Focs'le hatch comes LONG JOAN SILVER—her of one leg, by the powers. She uses a wooden crutch with practiced ease and has a parrot on her shoulder...but did you really need me to tell you that?)

CAPTAIN SMOLLETT: A woman! On my crew!

JIM: She only has one leg!

CAPTAIN SMOLLETT: Most of a woman—on my crew!

SQUIRE TRELAWNEY: Don't mention it, Jim, but there's a tax rebate for hiring a handicapped woman.

CAPTAIN SMOLLETT: Sir, I protest.

SQUIRE TRELAWNEY: Protest all you like, and you can go hang for a scoundrel! It is my purse that's the lighter for this voyage, and you are in my employ!

THE PARROT: Darby, fetch aft the rum!

LONG JOAN SILVER: *(To the parrot:)* Shut it! *(To the others:)* Shipmates! Captain, Squire, pardon my familiarity, I didn't mean to interject myself amongst my betters when they be so deep in conference, like.

JIM: A one-legged sea-faring woman!

LONG JOAN SILVER: Aye...not the only one.

JIM: There can't be many—

LONG JOAN SILVER: I know all the sailors in Bristol young lad, says I. Many of 'em missing an arm or a leg, lost in the service of good King George or to the natural hazards which attend a life before the mast. Some of them are women, but not to be judged too harsh on that account, them not choosing it, ye understand...and I work as hard as any able bodied man, ye may lay to that. *(To the Squire:)* The galley's well founded, Squire—plenty of rum aboard as per your orders, salt beef and hard tack for the crew, eight brace of partridges, six suckling porkers and a cask of foie gras for yourself and the other officers.

SQUIRE TRELAWNEY: The morels?

LONG JOAN SILVER: Out of season, I'm afraid—but I laid in some white truffles in oil, and I can make do.

SQUIRE TRELAWNEY: There—Captain, could you ask for a finer sea-cook?

CAPTAIN SMOLLETT: A woman, before the mast? Are you mad, sir?

(Israel Hands and Maria Lindsey enter struggling over the railing with a huge barrel.)

CAPTAIN SMOLLETT: What now?

LONG JOAN SILVER: I took the liberty of ordering a barrel of apples, sir. Admiral Hawke always kept a barrel of apples lashed to the mast, he did—for the crew to dip into. Never a sign of scurvy amongst the hands.

DR. LIVESEY: A capital idea—although lemons or limes would be richer in ascorbic acid.

LONG JOAN SILVER: Couldn't do that, Doctor. Elsewise, a hundred years from now they'll start calling us lemonies or something.

DR. LIVESEY: Give them a while. *(Beat.)* They got it... How did you know I was a doctor?

LONG JOAN SILVER: I merely assumed you was a man of learning by your reference to ascorbic acid, sir.

DR. LIVESEY: Hmmm.

LONG JOAN SILVER: Where be the rest of the crew? Perhaps they'd like an apple.

SQUIRE TRELAWNEY: The crew has not yet been engaged.

LONG JOAN SILVER: There be a manner of problem?

CAPTAIN SMOLLETT: Aye—there's a problem—there's a woman aboard my ship! A woman on the crew always causes trouble.

LONG JOAN SILVER: I couldn't agree with you more, Captain.

CAPTAIN SMOLLETT: There you are, Squire. This woman knows—

LONG JOAN SILVER: One woman, that's true, sir. Two or more, and there's no issue.

SQUIRE TRELAWNEY: Interesting, but where would we ever—

LONG JOAN SILVER: Israel! Maria!

(Israel and Maria stop tying the barrel, and approach rapidly, saluting.)

Dab hands, they are, sirs, and I'll warrant they can out-sail any man I've ever known.

SQUIRE TRELAWNEY: There you are, Captain—two more fine sailors for the ship's list.

ISRAEL HANDS: Thanks be to ye, and I'm at your service.

SQUIRE TRELAWNEY: Yes, I think that's the point.

(Maria and Anne get back to the barrel. As they go:)

MARIA LINDSEY: *(Quietly mocking:)* Thanks be to ye, at your service, let me kiss yer behind while I'm at it.

(Israel smacks her.)

SQUIRE TRELAWNEY: *(To Joan:)* Do you know any other able crew?

LONG JOAN SILVER: I could scare up a dozen quicker than a handsplice, aye. They may not be much to look at, but they know their sails.

SQUIRE TRELAWNEY: Hire them! Fetch them immediately, and we can sail on the evening tide!

LONG JOAN SILVER: Aye aye, sir! leave

CAPTAIN SMOLLETT: Squire—

SQUIRE TRELAWNEY: I feel we have been over this, Captain! I wish to sail on the next tide! If we do it with a crew of women, so be it. Plus, we only need to pay them seventy pence on the pound, so that's a savings right there.

LONG JOAN SILVER: A penny saved be a penny earned, says I, your grace. Perhaps the cabin boy can help me with the longboat. Two row quicker than one says I, and we will return all the sooner with your crew, says you.

DR. LIVESEY: A capital idea, um—Joan, was it?

LONG JOAN SILVER: Long Joan Silver—but me shipmates call me Silver.

DR. LIVESEY: Silver it is. Go on, Jim, into the boat with her.

JIM: *(To Silver:)* Did you know a sailor named Sally? Sally Bones?

LONG JOAN SILVER: Sally Bones? Cap'n Sally Bones, had a tattoo of a snake biting an anchor, and a fondness for rum?

JIM: I never saw her tattoo.

LONG JOAN SILVER: I should hope not, at your age.

JIM: So you know—

LONG JOAN SILVER: Never heard of her. *(Beat.)* Just luffin' yer sails, lad—I know every sailor in Bristol said I, and meant it I did.

JIM: She used to speak of a one-legged sea-faring woman. A right villain, she called her.

LONG JOAN SILVER: Aye, she mentioned her once or twice. One-legged woman wi' a heart as black as bilgewater—last I heard, she was cooper on a whaling ship, off the coast of Peru. And?

JIM: Never mind. *(Beat.)* Where was the tattoo?

LONG JOAN SILVER: I never knew her well enough to ask.

JIM: Oh. My word.

DR. LIVESEY: Perhaps you should let the boy row. Some healthy exercise?

LONG JOAN SILVER: Step lively, laddie—into the longboat and we'll be ashore in a trice.

(Jim and Silver go to the railing.)

JIM: You...uh, your...well...can I ask you something...your um...well...

(He indicates her missing leg. He might do this for a while, getting more and more awkward as Silver doesn't respond. Eventually:)

LONG JOAN SILVER: Out with it, Lad.

JIM: Um...why don't you have a leg?

(A long pause.)

LONG JOAN SILVER: I do have a leg.

(They climb over the railing. Lights out.)

SCENE 4

(The dockside – a bustling marketplace. MERCHANTS sell items from carts to various SAILORS and a few of the pirates. Behind one cart, Blind Pew talks to Tess Morgan. Silver and Jim enter.)

THE PARROT: Pieces of Eight! Pieces of Eight!

LONG JOAN SILVER: Cap'n Flint—'er name is, after the famous pirate what terrorized the seven seas these many years hence.

(Jim goes to stroke the parrot. Casually:)

Don't touch 'er, son—she'll have yer finger. That bird be nigh two hundred years old. They live forever mostly; and none 'as seen more wickedness. She's seen good ships sunk and good sailors leaping off their burning decks. She learned 'Pieces of eight" at the fishing up of the wrecked plate ships—and little wonder; three hundred and fifty thousand of 'em, Hawkins! To look at her you would think she was a babby. But you smelt powder—didn't you, cap'n?

THE PARROT: Stand by to go about!

MEAT PIE SELLER: Meat pies! Get'chor meat pies 'ere! Fresh from that little barbershop in Fleet street—luverly meat pies, made with a little priest—*by* a little priest.

LONG JOAN SILVER: We'll find a few of me shipmates 'long the docks, I'll warrant.

MERCHANT OF THINGS: Things inside things! Ships in a bottle, limes in a coconut—get one fer the wife—genies in lamps.

JIM: A genie in a lamp?

MERCHANT OF THINGS: Different story, son. Move along... Pickles in brine! Tongues in cheek! Pigs in...a blanket!

FRUIT DEALER: Second hand fruit! Oranges, Lemons, Limes—only used once! Almost like new!

(Maria Lindsey steals a piece of fruit and runs off.)

Come back 'ere, you dang lemony!

(The Fruit Dealer gives chase and exits after her. All the other pirates quickly steal everything else off the cart. A couple grab the whole cart and run off with it, revealing Pew talking to Tess Morgan. Jim sees Pew.)

LONG JOAN SILVER: Close yer mouth, son—ye'll be catching flies.

JIM: Pew!

LONG JOAN SILVER: You step in something?

JIM: That woman! It's Blind Pew!

(Blind Pew hears that, turns and runs into a stall.)

LONG JOAN SILVER: What?

JIM: Stop her! It's Blind Pew!

(Blind Pew gets up, pushes the stall keeper aside and runs off stage. A CLATTERING of hooves, Pew screams, a HORSE WHINNIES in fear. Silver covers Jim's eyes.)

LONG JOAN SILVER: Don't look, me boy—that's not a fit sight for a young'un like yerself.

(Jim looks.)

JIM: Ew—gross!

LONG JOAN SILVER: Run down by a horse and cart, I swear.

JIM: We must fetch the doctor!

LONG JOAN SILVER: 'Tis no use, Jim lad. When a lass' brains are on the outside of her head like that, there's not much a sawbones can do 'cept charge her next of kin for a housecall. What be that name ye called her?

JIM: Pew. Blind Pew.

LONG JOAN SILVER: Not the most politically correct of names, but apt for the affliction, I'll grant ye.

JIM: Has Squire Trelawney not told you of the buccaneers? She was one of them!

LONG JOAN SILVER: One of those swabs, was she? Well, mayhap that horse saved the hangman some rope. *(To Tess Morgan:)* Tess! Tess Morgan, fetch yourself over here!

(Tess approaches.)

Now, Tess, you never clapped your eyes on that lady, Flat Pew-

JIM: Blind Pew—

LONG JOAN SILVER: Blind Pew, afore, did you now?

TESS MORGAN: No, ma'am, Silver ma'am—I met her just now in the street.

LONG JOAN SILVER: You didn't know her name, did you?

TESS MORGAN: Whose name?

LONG JOAN SILVER: Squashed Pew!

TESS MORGAN: Blind Pew.

LONG JOAN SILVER: Blind Pew, aye.

TESS MORGAN: Never heard of her before! Right? Or did I?

LONG JOAN SILVER: By the powers, Tess Morgan, it's as good for you, you hadn't! If you had been mixed up with the like of that, you would never be a shipmate of mine again, you may lay to that. *(Shooing her away from Jim:)* Go after the others, and tell'em: We'm be getting a crew for the Hispaniola. Tell'em all hands what knows me aboard by four bells. *(Quietly:)* If yer don't know the course, keep yer porthole shut, aye?

TESS MORGAN: Sorry, Silver.

(Tess talks to any remaining pirates and they exit after the others. Long Joan Silver turns to Jim.)

LONG JOAN SILVER: She's an honest sailor, Tess Morgan, but as dumb as a bag of rope. Less brains than Snuffed-it Pew over there.

JIM: Blind Pew.

LONG JOAN SILVER: I think it be a moot point, Jim me lad. We'd better report to the Captain, tell'im whatever these buccaneers are after, leastwise there's one less of 'em, eh Hawkins?

JIM: Aye...I guess there is.

LONG JOAN SILVER: Don't look so down hearted, me boy—people get squashed sometimes. Part o' the great circle of life—goes round an' round, just like her kidney on that cart wheel.

JIM: It just seems an ill omen of our voyage.

LONG JOAN SILVER: Ye've not stared death in the eye in your few years, I'll warrant. First time?

JIM: Third.

LONG JOAN SILVER: Third! And you so young.

JIM: Capn' Sally Bones just last week, and before her...my...my father—he passed on not a month ago.

LONG JOAN SILVER: Squashed, was he? Like her over there? Lying in a gutter, bloody hoofprints up his broken body, wi' his brains squirted out his ears like an overripe plum, an' his kidney still going round and—no wait, it came off.

JIM: No, no! He died quietly, in his sleep.

LONG JOAN SILVER: Can't ask for more than that, lad.

JIM: I miss him.

LONG JOAN SILVER: 'Course you do, lad—'course you do, him dying off all selfish-like when he should've been here to look after yer and teach yer how to be a man, eh? Well, bless yer heart, Jim—Long Joan Silver'll teach yer how to be a man! For sure and certain I will!

JIM: You'll show me how to be a man?

MRS. HAWKINS: *(From the back of the auditorium:)* Oh Lord! Please smite my son with a timorous disposition and steadfast buttons!

LONG JOAN SILVER: Strike my colors, but that woman has good hearing!

JIM: Tell me about it.

LONG JOAN SILVER: Make ye a man? I'll make ye a sailor, I will! I'll teach you proper oceancraft, me boy—learn you the ropes, and the ways of a ship on the high seas, aye?

JIM: That'd be fine, Mistress Silver!

LONG JOAN SILVER: Just Silver, Lad—Just Silver. You're a lad, you are, but you're as smart as paint. I see'd that when I first set eyes on you. But come now, stand by to go about. Dooty is dooty. I'll put on my old cockerel hat, pick up me watch coat and me kit bag, and step along of you to Cap'n Smollett, and report this here affair. He'll want to know the details and particulars—if those buccaneers are about, it'd be better if we had a good supply of arms.

THE PARROT: And an extra leg.

LONG JOAN SILVER: What?

THE PARROT: Pieces of eight! Pieces of eight!

(They exit. Lights out.)

SCENE 5

(Aboard the Hispaniola. First Mate ALAN ARROW directs the pirates as they carry muskets and barrels of gunpowder aboard.)

ARROW: Stow them muskets, ladies. Powder in the for'ard magazine! You!

ANNE BONNEY: Anne Bonney, sir.

ARROW: Lay on the blue ensign!

ANNE BONNEY: Aye aye, sir.

ARROW: Quick now—don't think I'll spare the whip for considerations of your dainty sex. Every sailor works their all on my ship, or they feel the end of a rope!

(He whips his cat o'nine tails in her direction as she fixes a blue flag with a union jack in the corner to the halyard. She hauls up the flag.)

ARROW: Stow them barrels, blast you! All hands ready to make sail on the quarter hour!

(TOM REDRUTH approaches Squire Trelawney.)

TOM REDRUTH: The Capting, sir, him be axing to 'aves a drib slack wit' ya, dracly-minute.

SQUIRE TRELAWNEY: He was axing...?

TOM REDRUTH: Aye, that 'im be.

SQUIRE TRELAWNEY: With an axe?

TOM REDRUTH: Wiv wot?

SQUIRE TRELAWNEY: I have no idea what you're saying.

TOM REDRUTH: Duz ya talks English, guv? ENG-LISH. DOES YER TALKS IT, LIKE?

(Tom points at the Captain.)

SQUIRE TRELAWNEY: Oik.

TOM REDRUTH: Toff.

(Squire Trelawney goes to Captain Smollett—who studies a chart at the stern. Dr. Livesy is nearby.)

SQUIRE TRELAWNEY: You wanted to give me an axe or something?

CAPTAIN SMOLLETT: Merely asked to speak to you, at your convenience.

SQUIRE TRELAWNEY: Now is convenient, Captain Smollett, what have you to say? All's well, I hope; all shipshape and seaworthy?

CAPTAIN SMOLLETT: Before we haul anchor, I better speak plain, even at the risk of offence. I don't like this cruise and I don't like the crew. That's short and sweet.

SQUIRE TRELAWNEY: Possibly, sir, you may not like your employer, either?

(Dr. Livesy hurries over.)

DR. LIVESEY: Stay a bit—no use of such questions as that but to produce ill feeling. The captain has said too much or he has said too little, and I'm bound to say that I require an explanation of his words. You don't, you say, like this cruise. Now, why?

CAPTAIN SMOLLETT: I'll sail under sealed orders, sirs, where you bid me—but now I find these blasted women before the mast know more than I do. I don't call that fair, now, do you?

DR. LIVESEY: *(Staring at Trelawney:)* No, I don't. Someone must've talked when they were told to keep their mouths shut.

(A long pause before Squire Trelawney notices Livesy's attention. Maybe a double take.)

SQUIRE TRELAWNEY: I say, are you accusing me?

DR. LIVESEY: I have kept as silent as the grave.

SQUIRE TRELAWNEY: Might've been the boy.

DR. LIVESEY: I impressed upon him the importance of keeping this close to our vests.

SQUIRE TRELAWNEY: As did I, Doctor—and to think that impudent snapper has been telling all and sundry. Probably he was drunk.

DR. LIVESEY: I think not.

CAPTAIN SMOLLETT: The how of it don't matter. They're saying we're going after treasure—heard it from my own crew, mind you. Now, treasure is ticklish work; I don't like treasure voyages on any account, and I don't like them, above all, when they are secret and when the secret has been told to the parrot!

SQUIRE TRELAWNEY: Silver's parrot?

CAPTAIN SMOLLETT: Just an expression.

SQUIRE TRELAWNEY: Lucky she has a parrot, then. Otherwise your expression would be silly.

CAPTAIN SMOLLETT: Blabbed, I mean. It's my belief neither of you gentlemen know what you are about, but I'll tell you the way of a voyage after treasure—life or death, and a close run.

SQUIRE TRELAWNEY: That's as may be, but the treasure will not go to a Hindu Ashram and spend its time in meditation!

(The others look confused.)

It's not going to find itself, Captain!

DR. LIVESEY: That is all clear, and, I dare say, true enough. We have chosen to take the risk. You say you don't like the crew. They may be women, but are they not good sailors?

CAPTAIN SMOLLETT: Women aboard is trouble, sir, and I don't like how they talk amongst themselves.

SQUIRE TRELAWNEY: What, high-pitched and giggly? I recall girls giggling when I was a schoolboy. Dashed unnerving it was too.

CAPTAIN SMOLLETT: Not these women, Squire. I'd say they're the least gigglingest crew I've ever seen. Not that any of the others were what you call prone to it—but this crew...they mutter. Quietly.

DR. LIVESEY: Tell us what you want.

CAPTAIN SMOLLETT: Gentlemen, are you determined to go on this cruise?

SQUIRE TRELAWNEY: Like iron.

CAPTAIN SMOLLETT: Then, as you've heard me very patiently, saying things that I could not prove, hear me a few words more. They are putting the powder and the arms in the fore hold. Now, you have a good place under the cabin; why not put them there? Then, you are bringing your servants with you—

DR. LIVESEY: *(To Trelawney:)* Really?

SQUIRE TRELAWNEY: We may be at sea, but I still have standards! Would you have me polishing my own boots, doctor?

DR. LIVESEY: Heaven forbid.

CAPTAIN SMOLLETT: As I was saying—

SQUIRE TRELAWNEY: These are Italian. I might ruin them.

CAPTAIN SMOLLETT: The servants—

SQUIRE TRELAWNEY: Polish them wrong, they explode you know.

DR. LIVESEY: I'm sure that's not true.

SQUIRE TRELAWNEY: Heard it from London's finest boot polisher myself.

CAPTAIN SMOLLETT: *(Interrupting:)* They tell me your servants are to be berthed forward. Why not give them berths aft beside the cabin?

SQUIRE TRELAWNEY: One of them's a little smelly.

CAPTAIN SMOLLETT: Open a porthole.

SQUIRE TRELAWNEY: I had no idea a sea voyage could demand such deprivations.

CAPTAIN SMOLLETT: One more item—there's been too much blabbing already.

DR. LIVESEY: Far too much.

SQUIRE TRELAWNEY: It's all Jim, I tell you.

CAPTAIN SMOLLETT: I've heard that you have a map of an island, that there's a cross on the map to show where treasure is, and that the island lies 36 degrees 7 minutes 27 seconds North and 115 degrees 10 minutes 12 seconds West.

SQUIRE TRELAWNEY: Lucky guess.

DR. LIVESEY: Squire!

SQUIRE TRELAWNEY: I never told *that* to a soul! I can never remember numbers.

DR. LIVESEY: It doesn't much matter who it was.

CAPTAIN SMOLLETT: I don't know who has this map; but I make it a point it shall be kept secret even from me and the ship's officers. Otherwise I would ask you to let me resign.

DR. LIVESEY: It becomes clear. You wish to make a garrison of the stern part of the ship, manned with our own people, and provided with all the arms and powder on board. In other words, you fear a mutiny.

CAPTAIN SMOLLETT: No captain, sir, would be justified in going to sea at all if he had ground enough to say that. Some of these women may be honest; all may be for what I know. But I am responsible for the ship's safety and the life of every man jack aboard of her. And those women too, of course. I ask you to take certain precautions, that's all.

SQUIRE TRELAWNEY: I will do as you desire, but I think the worse of you, Captain. In my opinion, you are craven.

CAPTAIN SMOLLETT: You can think as you please. You'll find I do my duty.

(The Captain leaves them.)

DR. LIVESEY: He heh—duty.

SQUIRE TRELAWNEY: And you're a medical man?

DR. LIVESEY: Trelawney, contrary to all my notions, I believe you have managed to get two honest sailors on board with you—that man and Joan Silver.

SQUIRE TRELAWNEY: Silver, if you like, but as for that intolerable humbug, I declare I think his conduct unmanly, unsailorly, and downright un-English.

DR. LIVESEY: Understood.

ARROW: *(On deck:)* 'Way up the anchor! First crew—hoist the mains'!

(Arrow lashes his whip. The crew lay on a rope and haul up the main sail. As they do, Bosun Abraham Gray and the crew sing a call-and-response shanty. [Bosun Gray sings lines 1 & 3 solo, the crew all sing lines 2 & 4 of each verse.])

BOSUN GRAY AND THE CREW: *(Singing:)* We crossed the fifty with an acre of sail
Dance on the footlin's buckos
Swerved for a turtle, ran over a whale,
Haul in me buckos haul in—*ho*!

The ship's got rats and the mate has got fleas
Dance on the footlin's buckos
If you don't heed his whip, he might even say please
Haul in me buckos haul in—*ho*!

I'd rather be Captain, this job is too hard
Dance on the footlin's buckos
Me milkshake brings all the boys out to the yard*
Haul in me buckos haul in
Haul in me buckos, haul in—*ho*!

*(*This line is dated even as I write this, and feel free to substitute your own. Perhaps Tom Redruth chimes in with the line: "But I got woss, us allay's tarred" which makes sense in Sussex dialect. No one understands him anyway. The original shanty, with music, is appended. The mains'l unfurls:)*

JIM: We're off! Off to sea!

(Dr. Livesy runs to the rail and throws up. Lights out.)

SCENE 6

(Blue moonlight illuminates the Hispaniola as she sails through a dark sea. At the helm, Jacquotte steers. On deck, Long Joan Silver sings softly as she peels potatoes into a wooden pail. As she sings, Jim enters at the stern, and crosses to the deck.)

LONG JOAN SILVER: *(Singing:)* More was seen by the sternlight screen,
Yo ho ho and a bottle of rum,
Charting no doubt where a woman had been,
Yo heave ho and a bottle of rum.
'Twas a flimsy shift on a bunker cot
With a thin dirk slot through the bosom spot
And the lace stiff dry with a purplish blot.
Oh, was she a wench, some shuddering maid
That dared the knife and took the blade,
Bedamn, she had stuff for a plucky jade,
Yo heave ho and a bottle of—

(Sees Jim and breaks off:)

Jim lad, there ye are!

JIM: What was that song?

LONG JOAN SILVER: Just an old sea shanty. I knows a hundred of 'em. Pull up alongside, bucko, give us a hand with these.

JIM: Aye, Silver.

(Jim sits, heavily.)

LONG JOAN SILVER: Missing your home, Jim? Yer mother?

JIM: A little. It's unfamiliar is all, to see nothing about us to the horizon. Days...weeks...nothing but sea and sky. I can't help but wonder about Mister Arrow.

LONG JOAN SILVER: Aye, Arrow. He were a fine sailor. A mite free with his whip, but a fine sailor.

JIM: And he vanished! Lost overboard in the night, who knows where?

LONG JOAN SILVER: Most likely the ocean. *(Beat.)* That be a conundrum, sure enough. Perhaps he was so busy holding onto that whip of his, he forgot to hold on to the ship.

JIM: It just seems death hangs over this voyage like a storm cloud on the horizon. We're a long way from Black Hill Cove.

LONG JOAN SILVER: Turn yer lookouts skyward, Jim. I'll show ye which way yer home lies without map nor compass. See there? That be Orion.

JIM: Where?

LONG JOAN SILVER: Ye see the three that make up his belt? Aye, and his hands and feet, and a cutlass at his side? Across the equator, he'm be standing on his head! And below him, a cross. Aye, the cross in the southern latitudes, and the Northern star up here. Learn yer stars, bucko, and ye can chart a course by'em as good as any set by compass or sextant.

JIM: Silver...what *happened* to your leg?

LONG JOAN SILVER: I shaved it—how nice of you to notice. *(Beat.)* Only takes me half as long as it used to, so there's that, I suppose...I better hop down to the galley and get these on the cookstove or the gentry'll be waiting on their supper.

JIM: I can do that for you, Silver.

LONG JOAN SILVER: Nay, lad—fetch yerself an apple and 'fore I get back see if ye can find six stars that chart out a saucepan. *(Hinting:)* Look north.

(Long Joan Silver takes the pail of potatoes and exits at the foc'sle. Jim climbs up the barrel but can't reach...he tumbles inside it as Israel Hands, Mary Reade, Anne Bonney, Tess Morgan and Liz Patrickson enter from the foc'sle.)

ISRAEL HANDS: How long are we a-going to hold off cuttin' their throats!? I've had a'most enough o' Cap'n Smollett. I want to go into that cabin, I do.

ANNE BONNEY: Aye—kill'em all. I want their food and wine!

(Jim looks out, horrified...and quickly ducks out of sight again as the pirates settle down nearby.)

MARY READE: We're down on the gundeck eatin' hardtack with weevils in it, they're up there wi' roast beef on a silver platter!

LIZ PATRICKSON: Kill the blaggards, says I. Why wait?

TESS MORGAN: You can knock them out.

LIZ PATRICKSON: Cut them down, I will.

TESS MORGAN: The weevils.

LIZ PATRICKSON: Howzat?

TESS MORGAN: Knock them out of the 'ardtack. Bang it on the table, the weevils, they come right out. *(Beat.)* It's like you're knockin' on a door, and they say: Hello! Who is it? *(Beat.)* You don't answer. They come out the 'ardtack, on the table.

LIZ PATRICKSON: I'll knock your head, I will.

TESS MORGAN: What did I say?

(Long Joan Silver enters.)

LONG JOAN SILVER: Cheerly, messmates. Where be the sprog?

TESS MORGAN: He's not here.

LONG JOAN SILVER: I can see that.

ISRAEL HANDS: Probably went to 'is fancy cabin aft, with his soft bed.

ANNE BONNEY: And no weevils in his hardtack.

MARY READE: In his roast beef.

LONG JOAN SILVER: Weevils, is it?

ISRAEL HANDS: Aye. *(Beat.)* When?

LONG JOAN SILVER: Israel, your head ain't much account, nor ever was. But you're able to hear, I reckon— leastways, your ears are big enough. Now, here's what I say: you'll berth forward, and you'll live hard, and you'll speak soft, and you'll keep sober till I give the word.

ISRAEL HANDS: Well, I don't say no, do I? What I say is, when? That's what I say.

LONG JOAN SILVER: When! The last moment I can manage, and that's when. Here's a first-rate navvy, Cap'n Smollett, sails the blessed ship for us. Here's this squire and doctor with a map and such—I don't know where it is, do I? No more do you, says you. We let them find the treasure, and help us to get it aboard, by the powers. For my druthers, I'd have Cap'n Smollett navigate us half-way back again afore I struck.

TESS MORGAN: We're all sailors.

LONG JOAN SILVER: We're all forec'sle hands, you mean—we can steer a course, but who's to set one? That's what you split on, first and last. I'd have Cap'n Smollett work us back into the trades at least; then we'd have no blessed miscalculations and a spoonful of water a day...but I know the sort you are. We'll finish with 'em at the island as soon's the treasure's on board, and a pity it is. Split my sides, I've a sick heart to sail with the likes of you!

LIZ PATRICKSON: Easy all, Silver, who's a-crossin' of you?

LONG JOAN SILVER: How many tall ships have I seen laid aboard? How many brisk lads and ladies drying in the sun at Execution Dock? And all for this same hurry and hurry and hurry. If you would on'y lay your course, and a point to windward, you would ride in carriages, you would. But not you! You'll have your mouthful of rum today, and tomorrow can go hang.

ISRAEL HANDS: I never met a messmate such as you, Silver. Call yourself a pirate.

TESS MORGAN: Most of a pirate.

LONG JOAN SILVER: What?

TESS MORGAN: You've only got one leg. *(Beat.)* Hadn't you noticed?

LONG JOAN SILVER: Now that you mention it...

(Silver backhands Tess.)

TESS MORGAN: Ow!

LONG JOAN SILVER: *(To Israel:)* Where are yer messmates now? Pew was that sort, and she died a beggar. Flint died of rum at Savannah. They was a sweet crew, they was! On'y, where are they?

TESS MORGAN: She hit me!

ANNE BONNEY: Shut yer porthole.

LIZ PATRICKSON: When we do lay 'em athwart, what are we to do with 'em, anyhow?

ISRAEL HANDS: Pitch'em over the side, like I did Mr. Arrow. Ground his fingers as he clung to the railing, I did.

TESS MORGAN: We could maroon'em. Like old Jennifer Gunn. We left her to die and rot all alone. "Bye bye" I waved as we sailed away, "Won't be seeing you agin!"

ANNE BONNEY: I say cut 'em down like that much pork. That would have been Flint's way, or Sally Bones'.

MARY READE: Sally always went straight to it. "Dead men don't bite," says she.

LONG JOAN SILVER: Well, she's dead herself; she knows the long and short on it now. I'm a peaceful soul at 'eart, says I, and would never wish harm to so much as a hair on their heads—but dooty is dooty, mates, so we kill'em. When I'm in Parlyment and riding in my coach, I don't want none of these sea-lawyers in the cabin turning up unlooked for, like a rat in yer wedding cake. Wait is what I say; but when the time comes, let her rip!

ISRAEL HANDS: Aye! Kill and burn'em all—honest men.

ANNE BONNEY: Aye!

LONG JOAN SILVER: Only one thing I claim—I claim Trelawney. I want to hold me fingers around his throat 'til his leg stops twitching, I do.

(The others laugh. Miss Bean enters at the stern and approaches.)

ANNE BONNEY: Hush!

MARY READE: Who goes there?

ISRAEL HANDS: Mistress Bean—come to see how a working woman lives, 'ave ye?

MISS BEAN: I've better things to see than that, Israel Hands. Come to fetch an apple for the Squire.

(She goes to the barrel.)

LONG JOAN SILVER: Set a while, Mistress. No hurry.

MISS BEAN: If I sit, it'll be on my account, not yours.

LONG JOAN SILVER: Go on. We sees how hard you work.

ANNE BONNEY: I've never seen her hauling canvas in a fierce blow—

LONG JOAN SILVER: Steady, shipmates. She be no sailor, true, but she works as hard as a powder monkey, and I sees that. All hours, fetching and carrying for the gen'lmen. At their whim, day or night.

(Miss Bean sits down.)

MISS BEAN: You've never said a truer word, cook.

LONG JOAN SILVER: Long hours for little thanks, I warrant.

MISS BEAN: Aye.

LONG JOAN SILVER: Off to sea—no choice of yours, wi' all the deprivations of a hard journey—and for what? A few farthings at the end of the week.

MISS BEAN: Very few.

LONG JOAN SILVER: You're young, you are, but you're as smart as paint. I see'd that when I first set me eyes on you, and I'll talk to you honest and open. Who works harder on this voyage, you or the Squire...? Nay, don't answer, there's none of us here need to have it said out. We all know. When this voyage comes back 'ome, who'll be turning up in Bristol wi' his pockets stuffed with gold, and who will be sweatin' down the gangplank under his blasted sea chest of Italian boots? *(Beat.)* There comes a time, lass, when a choice can be made.

MISS BEAN: Not many choices in life for the likes of us.

LONG JOAN SILVER: There's always a choice. There was some that was feared of Pew, and some that was feared of Flint; but Flint only ever feared one person, and you're lookin' at her.

TESS MORGAN: Flint was afeared of me?

(Anne smacks her upside the head.)

LONG JOAN SILVER: We were the roughest crew afloat—and all of us women. *All* of us.

MISS BEAN: Cap'n Flint wasn't...she was a woman!?

LONG JOAN SILVER: Aye. Won't read that in the broadsheets, but I sailed with her. Ran off to sea as a young maid, she did, put on a pair of breeches and took on the world. The finest captain I ever seen. Out on the open ocean, there were no men tellin' us what was what. I'm not boastful, and you seen yourself how easy I keep company, but when I was quartermaster, lambs wasn't the word for Mistress Flint's old buccaneers, nor serving girls nor maids neither. No guvnor. No orders but what the one givin'em is hauling a rope alongside ye. Ye may be sure of yourself in Long Joan Silver's ship.

MISS BEAN: Your ship?

LONG JOAN SILVER: If it were so, would you be alongside of us? Will ye sail with us, and return to Bristol with pockets stuffed with gold of your own?

TESS MORGAN: And no boots.

MISS BEAN: I quite like boots.

LONG JOAN SILVER: Boots of your own. Italian ones. *(Pause.)* Think on it. The Squire is waiting on his apple.

MISS BEAN: Oh! His apple!

(Miss Bean jumps up, goes to the barrel – reaches in. Can't reach. She hikes herself up, just as she is about to look into it – she turns back.)

MISS BEAN: Damn his apple. He can go hungry.

LONG JOAN SILVER: That's me girl.

ANNE BONNEY: I say this calls for a go of the rum.

MARY READE: Aye!

MISS BEAN: I wouldn't say no.

LONG JOAN SILVER: Aye, messmates—just a tot, mind—below, and quick.

(They exit at the focs'le. Jim crawls out of the barrel.)

JIM: Mutiny!

(He hurries to the stern.)

JACQUOTTE DELCHARGE: All is well?

JIM: I need to see the Captain.

JACQUOTTE DELCHARGE: But does the *Capitaine* wish to see you?

JIM: I must pass.

JACQUOTTE DELCHARGE: Perhaps you should give me ze massage.

JIM: Give you a what?

JACQUOTTE DELCHARGE: Ze massage.

JIM: Like, rubbing all over your...I mean, touching your...um...form.

(A beat. Jim suddenly leaps up on the railing, listening intently.)

Did you hear that?

JACQUOTTE DELCHARGE: I hear nozzing.

JIM: Me neither. *(Beat.)* I'm alone. I mean, on my own.

(Captain Smollett enters.)

CAPTAIN SMOLLETT: All well?

JACQUOTTE DELCHARGE: The wind—she turns, *Capitaine,* and twice I smelled land on the breeze. Any day now.

CAPTAIN SMOLLETT: A quiet night and a fair breeze.

JACQUOTTE DELCHARGE: The boy here 'as a massage for you. And 'e is, apparently, 'earing things. Well, *not* 'earing things. But he is not 'earing them *very much* so.

CAPTAIN SMOLLETT: I'll take her. You're relieved, Jacquotte.

JACQUOTTE DELCHARGE: *Capitaine,* I can sail the rest of my watch—

CAPTAIN SMOLLETT: I said you're relieved, sailor! Utter blithering—are you drunk?

JACQUOTTE DELCHARGE: I am French, *Capitaine.*

CAPTAIN SMOLLETT: Even worse. Go below.

(Jacquotte goes, slowly, past Jim – suspicious.)

Well, lad?

JIM: I must speak to you, and the Doctor.

CAPTAIN SMOLLETT: You look like your breeches are on fire. Can it not wait until morning?

JIM: No sir.

CAPTAIN SMOLLETT: It's not about—thingy, is it?

JIM: Thingy?

CAPTAIN SMOLLETT: Bodily...dreams. Of a sort.

JIM: No.

CAPTAIN SMOLLETT: Thank heavens.

(On deck, Jacquotte suddenly leaps on the railing, staring out to sea.)

JACQUOTTE DELCHARGE: Land, *Capitaine*! LAND-HO!

CAPTAIN SMOLLETT: LAND-HO! ALL HANDS ON DECK!

(The crew enter first, then officers and servants, then Dr. Livesy, finally Squire Trelawney in the most ridiculous dressing gown and nightcap, lining the rail, excited.)

There she lies, right on course! Bosun—sheet home, if you please!

BOSUN GRAY: Sheet home, all hands!

THE CREW: Aye, aye!

(The crew lays on a rope.)

TOM REDRUTH: Arh, dat isle, standin' be an' all pert like.

SQUIRE TRELAWNEY: Well said.

CAPTAIN SMOLLETT: Has any one of you ever seen that land ahead?

LONG JOAN SILVER: I have, sir, I've watered there with a trader I was cook in.

CAPTAIN SMOLLETT: The anchorage is on the south, behind an islet, I fancy?

LONG JOAN SILVER: Yes, sir; Skeleton Island they calls it. A hand we had on board knowed all their names for it. That big hill with the cloud on it—he called it the Spy-glass, by reason of a lookout they kept when they was in the anchorage.

CAPTAIN SMOLLETT: I have a chart here. See if that's the place.

(As Silver takes the chart, all the pirates break off to stare—whispering and muttering among themselves: The map! It's the map!)

LONG JOAN SILVER: This chart...the ink's wet.

DR. LIVESEY: Is it now?

LONG JOAN SILVER: Aye. No names on it at all. *(More to the crew:)* No markings neither. Though very prettily drawn out, recent-like. *(To Captain Smollett:)* Here—Cap'n Kidd's Anchorage, my shipmate called it. There's a strong current runs along the south, and then away nor'ard up the west coast. Right you was, sir, to haul your wind and keep the weather of the island.

CAPTAIN SMOLLETT: Thank you, Silver.

LONG JOAN SILVER: *(To Jim:)* This here is a sweet spot for a lad to get ashore on. An old stockade to explore, and rivers to swim, and trees to climb... Why, it makes me young again. *(Beat.)* I almost forgot me timber leg. It's a pleasant thing to be young and have ten toes, and you may lay to that. When you want to go ashore, you just ask Joan, and she'll whip up a little PB and J—Pigeye Bass and Jellyfish—to take with you.

JIM: Aye.

CAPTAIN SMOLLETT: *(To Silver:)* You may go.

(As Silver hobbles to the deck, Jim goes to the Captain.)

JIM: Captain—get the Doctor and Squire down to the cabin, and then make some pretence to send for me. I have terrible news.

(A pause.)

CAPTAIN SMOLLETT: Gentlemen...I mean, ladies—this land we have sighted is the place we have been sailing for. Mr. Trelawney, being a very open-handed gentleman, has just asked me a word or two, and I was able to tell him that every lass on board had done her duty, alow and aloft, as I never ask to see it done better. At his suggestion, he and I and the doctor will go to the cabin to drink your health, and you'll have grog yourselves to drink our health!

SQUIRE TRELAWNEY: I said that?

CAPTAIN SMOLLETT: Aye.

SQUIRE TRELAWNEY: I don't think I did.

CAPTAIN SMOLLETT: You did.

SQUIRE TRELAWNEY: My rum?

CAPTAIN SMOLLETT: *(To the crew:)* I'll tell you what I think of this: I think it handsome. And if you think as I do, you'll give a good sea-cheer for the gentleman that does it.

THE CREW: Huzzah!

SQUIRE TRELAWNEY: *(To Captain Smollett:)* You're very free with another man's rum.

LONG JOAN SILVER: One more cheer for Cap'n Smollett!

THE CREW: Huzzah!

CAPTAIN SMOLLETT: Thank ye all. Joan—a ration for every sailor aboard, and send young Hawkins to my cabin wi' a good measure for the officers.

LONG JOAN SILVER: Aye aye, Cap'n! *(Beat.)* Shiver me timbers, I left the potatoes on!

(As she hobbles at high speed for the foc'sle hatch: Lights out.)

SCENE 7

(A well appointed cabin, dimly lit. The Captain, the Doctor and the Squire wait impatiently. Jim enters, carrying a bottle of rum.)

SQUIRE TRELAWNEY: There's my rum. What's left of it.

CAPTAIN SMOLLETT: Belay that—the boy has news—and dark news, I'll warrant.

SQUIRE TRELAWNEY: What, that they've finished my rum?

JIM: In a word—mutiny, sirs.

SQUIRE TRELAWNEY: That's two words.

JIM: Just mutiny, then.

SQUIRE TRELAWNEY: Mutiny!

JIM: I heard them plotting. They mean to strike as soon as the treasure is found.

DR. LIVESEY: Who? Who is their ringleader?

JIM: *(Shattered by it:)* It's Silver. Long Joan Silver herself.

SQUIRE TRELAWNEY: Well, captain, you were right, and I was wrong. I own myself an ass, and I await your orders.

CAPTAIN SMOLLETT: No more an ass than I, sir. I never heard of a crew that meant to mutiny but what showed signs before, for any man that had an eye in his head to see the mischief and take steps according. But this crew beats me.

SQUIRE TRELAWNEY: You're right—you're the bigger ass.

DR. LIVESEY: It's that Silver. A most remarkable woman.

CAPTAIN SMOLLETT: She'd look remarkably well hanged from a yard-arm. *(Beat.)* We must go on. If I give the word to turn back, they would rise at once... But we have time before us—at least until this treasure's found. It'll come to blows sooner or later, but what I propose is to take time by the forelock, as the saying is, and strike first—when they least expect it. We can count on your servants, Mr. Trelawney?

SQUIRE TRELAWNEY: As upon myself.

JIM: Not Mistress Bean.

SQUIRE TRELAWNEY: My own servant?!

JIM: I heard her.

SQUIRE TRELAWNEY: Damme, I never got my apple, did I?

DR. LIVESEY: I don't think an apple is the point.

SQUIRE TRELAWNEY: I didn't say it was, I merely pointed out that my own servants cannot be trusted.

DR. LIVESEY: Missus Sitwell, perhaps.

SQUIRE TRELAWNEY: Aye—I'll ask her to fetch an apple, first thing.

CAPTAIN SMOLLETT: That's not really an absolute test.

SQUIRE TRELAWNEY: Two apples?

DR. LIVESEY: Jim—ye've spent time with the Squire's servants, running errands and so forth—you must know them better than anyone.

SQUIRE TRELAWNEY: I think I would know them—

DR. LIVESEY: You know them only as employer. Jim as friend. Tell us, lad—is there anything Missus Sitwell is afraid of?

JIM: Aye Doctor, now that you mention it...

DR. LIVESEY: Yes?

JIM: She lives in mortal peril of a man in a chicken suit, sir.

DR. LIVESEY: Really?

JIM: Aye—sometimes wakes up in the night, fearing a man in a chicken suit with only one arm and a tea kettle on his head, sir.

DR. LIVESEY: A tea kettle?

JIM: With a fish in it.

SQUIRE TRELAWNEY: What kind of fish?

JIM: A haddock.

SQUIRE TRELAWNEY: Curse me, we've only got smoked kippers aboard.

CAPTAIN SMOLLETT: Jim?

(A pause.)

JIM: I was lying, I just wanted to see if he'd go for it.

DR. LIVESEY: So there's no way to be sure.

CAPTAIN SMOLLETT: I reckon there are the four of us, the Bosun, the carpenter...maybe Missus Sitwell. Seven at best, and one of them just a lad. They are eleven.

SQUIRE TRELAWNEY: And to think that they're all English! I could find it in my heart to blow up the ship.

CAPTAIN SMOLLETT: The situation's dire, I'll grant ye—but there's no help for it till we know who stands with us. Lay to, and whistle for a wind, that's my view.

DR. LIVESEY: And end up trapped in this cabin? Holding the passageway 'gainst eleven bloodthirsty sea-wenches? We'll not last a night.

JIM: There's another option. Silver mentioned a stockade ashore.

CAPTAIN SMOLLETT: Hand me that chart—no, the real one.

DR. LIVESEY: You said you didn't want to know where it was hid.

CAPTAIN SMOLLETT: The time for that has passed. Hand it over.

DR. LIVESEY: Very well, but avert your eyes.

CAPTAIN SMOLLETT: What?

DR. LIVESEY: All of you. *(To the audience:)* You too. *(Back to the others:)* No one is to look while I retrieve the map from its dark and secret hiding place.

CAPTAIN SMOLLETT: So be it.

(Everyone covers their eyes. Dr. Livesy reaches into his jacket pocket and takes out the map.)

DR. LIVESEY: You may open your eyes now.

CAPTAIN SMOLLETT: Where...where was it hidden?

SQUIRE TRELAWNEY: Is it smelly?

DR. LIVESEY: It was hidden where none might think to look for it. I used reverse psychology.

SQUIRE TRELAWNEY: Reversed...? You mean, you stuck it up inside your—

DR. LIVESEY: No!

CAPTAIN SMOLLETT: Give me the map. *(He takes it warily—fingertips:)* There—marked clearly, a stockade. That's our course, Gentlemen—take what guns, powder and shot we can, sneak out under cover of night, into a longboat and haul for shore.

DR. LIVESEY: A capital plan.

CAPTAIN SMOLLETT: Wi' any luck, we'll make it ashore before anyone sees us, hears the boat being lowered or our oars in the water; and none think to turn the ship and have at us with the cannon.

SQUIRE TRELAWNEY: We're dead.

(Lights out.)

END OF ACT I

(During the intermission, someone in a chicken suit chases Mrs. Sitwell across the stage and up and down the aisles. Just if there's one handy, o'course.)

ACT II

SCENE 1

(The Stockade—a rough log block house. Morning light shines through the gun ports. Sounds of GUNFIRE, CANNONBALLS, SHOT WHISTLING PAST. Trelawney, Livesy, Gray, Smollett, Sitwell, and Jim enter into the stockade, screaming all the way and slam the door shut behind them.)

DR. LIVESEY: Wasn't too bad.

CAPTAIN SMOLLETT: Did we lose anyone?

DR. LIVESEY: Aye, Tom Redruth, the carpenter.

(An approaching scream gets louder:)

The door!

(The Captain opens the door, as Tom Redruth runs in, full tilt, screaming all the way. The Captain slams the door shut.)

SQUIRE TRELAWNEY: You made it.

TOM REDRUTH: Dem's dat knows 'ows I run, they wouldn't a' believed as hows I'd dun it...but dems dat seed me do it, they beleft.

SQUIRE TRELAWNEY: Whatever you just said, congratulations.

CAPTAIN SMOLLETT: To the musket ports—quick! Dr. Livesey take the north side, if you please; Tom, the east; Gray, west.

SQUIRE TRELAWNEY: I'll just curl up in the corner.

CAPTAIN SMOLLETT: We'll need you and Missus Sitwell center—reloading. As a man passes you a musket, reload and back to'em, quick as you can.

(They look out the musket ports in the walls.)

MRS. SITWELL: In the middle, where any stray bullet making it through any gun port is sure to pass.

CAPTAIN SMOLLETT: Aye.

MRS. SITWELL: With an open barrel of gunpowder next to us.

CAPTAIN SMOLLETT: Aye.

MRS. SITWELL: I'm so glad I chose this side.

CAPTAIN SMOLLETT: Any sign of 'em?

BOSUN GRAY: Movement in the trees!

(A gunshot rings out – everyone ducks.)

SQUIRE TRELAWNEY: Now the trees are shooting at us?!

(They fire back. A pause – the gunfire ceases.)

LONG JOAN SILVER: (*Off:*) Flag of truce!

DR. LIVESEY: That's Silver. She's holding a white flag.

CAPTAIN SMOLLETT: Ten to one this is a trick.

SQUIRE TRELAWNEY: I'll take those odds.

CAPTAIN SMOLLETT: Just an expression.

SQUIRE TRELAWNEY: You and your expressions!

DR. LIVESEY: *(Yelling out the gun port:)* What do you want with your flag of truce?

LONG JOAN SILVER: *(Off:)* Cap'n Silver, sir, to come on board and make terms.

CAPTAIN SMOLLETT: *Captain* Silver? Never heard of *him.*

TOM REDRUTH: *(To the others:)* Cook to capting! Eh, dat dere's affirmative action for yeh.

LONG JOAN SILVER: *(Off:)* That'd be me, sir. These poor ladies have chosen me cap'n, after your *desertion,* sirs. We can come to terms—all I ask is your word, Cap'n Smollett, to let me safe and sound out of the stockade, and one minute to get out o' shot before a gun is fired.

CAPTAIN SMOLLETT: I have not the slightest desire to talk to you. If you wish to talk to me, you can come. If there's any treachery, it'll be on your side, and the Lord help you.

LONG JOAN SILVER: *(Off:)* A word from you's enough. I knows a gentleman, and you may lay to that.

(Silver enters, carrying a grubby white handkerchief tied to a stick.)

CAPTAIN SMOLLETT: That's far enough. On the ground.

LONG JOAN SILVER: It's a main cold morning, to be sure, sir, to sit upon the ground.

CAPTAIN SMOLLETT: You might have been sitting in your galley, safe and warm. You're either my ship's cook and treated handsome, or Cap'n Silver, a common mutineer and pirate, and then you can go sit on the cold ground, and I hope you get a cold bottom!

LONG JOAN SILVER: Ye'll have to give me a hand up again, that's all.

(She sits.)

A sweet pretty place you have of it here. Ah, there's Jim! The top of the morning to ye, Jim. Doctor, here's my service. Why, there ye all are together like a happy family, in a manner of speaking.

CAPTAIN SMOLLETT: If you have anything to say, woman, better say it.

LONG JOAN SILVER: We want that treasure, and we'll have it. You'm would just as soon save yer lives, I reckon. I propose a trade. Ye have the chart, haven't ye?

CAPTAIN SMOLLETT: That's as may be.

SQUIRE TRELAWNEY: Although you don't want to know where.

LONG JOAN SILVER: All contrarywise, that be exactly what I want. Give us the chart to get the treasure and we'll offer you a choice. Either ye come aboard along of us, and upon my word of honour, we'll set ye somewhere safe ashore. Or if that ain't to your fancy, some of my ladies having old scores on account of your hiring an officer over-handy with a whip, then you can stay here. We'll divide the ship's stores with you, even-like, and the first ship I sight, I send 'em here to pick you up.

CAPTAIN SMOLLETT: Is that all?

LONG JOAN SILVER: Every last word, by thunder! Refuse it, and ye've seen the last of me but musket-balls.

CAPTAIN SMOLLETT: Then hear me. If you'll come up one by one, unarmed, I'll engage to clap you all in irons and take you home to a fair trial in England. If you won't, my name is Alexander Smollett, and I'll see you all to Davy Jones. You can't find the treasure. You can't leave the island—your ship's in irons, Mistress Silver; you're on a lee shore, trapped, and there's not a woman among you fit to sail her. I stand here and tell you so; and they're the last good words you'll get from me, for I'll put a bullet through your head when next I meet you, trollop. Get out.

LONG JOAN SILVER: Give me a hand up.

CAPTAIN SMOLLETT: Not I!

LONG JOAN SILVER: Who'll give me a hand up?! *(Beat.)* Jim?

(No one moves. Silver crawls to the doorway and pulls herself up.)

Before an hour's out, I'll see your blood on the sand. Them that die'll be the lucky ones.

(She exits.)

SQUIRE TRELAWNEY: She's utterly wrong—surely dying is *un*lucky. She got that backwards. No sense at all.

DR. LIVESEY: She said within the hour—d'ye think we have time to—

LONG JOAN SILVER: *(Off:)* At 'em, all hands! Tear'em apart!

(More gunfire. Bosun Gray aims his musket – and it is snatched from his grasp – a hand grabs him through the port!)

BOSUN GRAY: They're upon us!

(Muskets poke in through the gun ports and fire. Smoke fills the air. Maria Lindsey appears in the doorway with a cutlass.)

MARIA LINDSEY: Kill'em all! Cut'em to pieces!

(Captain Smollett fires his pistol – she falls.)

CAPTAIN SMOLLETT: We're trapped in here! Out, lads, out, and fight 'em in the open! Cutlasses!

(They exit. The muskets disappear from the port holes. The sounds of fighting outside.)

DR. LIVESEY: *(Off:)* Round the corner, lads! Round the stockade!

JIM: *(Off:)* Look to your right, doctor! More of 'em!

(More fighting sounds:)

TOM REDRUTH: *(Off:)* Dem be 'ere's an all! All's on rahnd de corner!

DR. LIVESEY: *(Off:)* They're out the back, as well! Round the next corner too, chaps!

(More fighting sounds:)

BOSUN GRAY: *(Off:)* They'm 'ere as well, blast'em! All the way 'round!

DR. LIVESEY: *(Off:)* Next corner!

JIM: *(Off:)* They're here too!

SQUIRE TRELAWNEY: *(Off:)* Back in the stockade! Back in the stockade!

(Everyone except Tom Redruth runs back in...including Tess Morgan, who somehow hasn't realized she's joined the wrong team. Mrs. Sitwell slumps against a wall—perhaps out of breath, but unnoticed by the others.)

CAPTAIN SMOLLETT: Well, that was a fire drill.

(Dr. Livesy examines his coat—slashed with a sword cut. He checks himself—no blood.)

DR. LIVESEY: Close it was, far too close.

BOSUN GRAY: Let's not be doin' that again!

TESS MORGAN: Aye, I almost got on the wrong side of 'em.

(A beat. Tess realizes at the same time as the others. Tess and the Captain clash—a brief sword fight and she cuts his leg, taking him down. As she's about to strike—the Squire stabs her in the back with his cutlass.)

Oh bloody'ell.

(Tess dies.)

SQUIRE TRELAWNEY: Are you much injured, Captain?

CAPTAIN SMOLLETT: It's not good, but I'll...Missus Sitwell?

MRS. SITWELL: I was hit.

(She takes her hand away from her stomach – she's bleeding.)

SQUIRE TRELAWNEY: Missus Sitwell!

(He catches her as she falls.)

MRS. SITWELL: I think I'm done for.

SQUIRE TRELAWNEY: Don't talk rot woman, you'll be just... *(He checks:)* Oh, that's bad. That's really, really—

DR. LIVESEY: Squire...

SQUIRE TRELAWNEY: No, it's awful. I can see her inside bits, and rather nasty they look too. This is beyond even your art, Doctor. *(To Sitwell:)* You're going to die for sure, um... *(He doesn't know her first name:)* Uh...Missus Sitwell.

MRS. SITWELL: Frances.

SQUIRE TRELAWNEY: Frances.

(She dies.)

JIM: We lost Tom Redruth, too. He never made it back in.

(An approaching SCREAM outside:)

DR. LIVESEY: *(Looking out:)* No—there he is! Quick, the—

(A LOUD GUN SHOT – the SCREAM cuts off abruptly:)

Never mind.

(Dr. Livesy turns away—and realizes his jacket has been cut open right at the pocket – he checks.)

The map! It fell! It's outside.

SQUIRE TRELAWNEY: My, you were scared.

(Bosun Gray dashes to a gun port:)

BOSUN GRAY: They have it. They're running off.

CAPTAIN SMOLLETT: Some of them—there's a couple of 'em will never run again.

SQUIRE TRELAWNEY: They'll take the treasure, and leave us here.

CAPTAIN SMOLLETT: First ship that ever I lost.

SQUIRE TRELAWNEY: And the treasure.

DR. LIVESEY: And Missus Sitwell.

SQUIRE TRELAWNEY: And the smelly one too. And my apple!

JIM: Spy glass hill!

DR. LIVESEY: What of it?

JIM: The water barrels in the Hispaniola. Did you see them?

SQUIRE TRELAWNEY: What water barrels?

JIM: Down in the orlop.

SQUIRE TRELAWNEY: Not going to catch me going down there. Euch.

CAPTAIN SMOLLETT: What about the water, Jim?

JIM: Green, and not much of it. If they're taking the ship, they'll look to provision her, take on water for the voyage.

SQUIRE TRELAWNEY: Aye. So?

JIM: They'll take her to a likely cove to set ashore with the barrels. If we have a lookout on Spyglass Hill, we can sight the anchorage, be on the shore to meet'em—pin'em down while they're in the longboat, maybe even our odds.

DR. LIVESEY: With a barrel of luck, we could take the ship back.

SQUIRE TRELAWNEY: But who will take the risk? They might have left a watch out there—whichever dashed fool tries it will get shot trying to get clear of the stockade!

CAPTAIN SMOLLETT: I'd go—but I can't, not with my leg like this.

BOSUN GRAY: My duty is to my captain. They'll not risk leaving us as witnesses—they mean to end us for sure. When those beggars come back, I'll hold'em off as long as I can. We'll go down fighting, we will.

CAPTAIN SMOLLETT: You're a good man, Gray. We'll be over-run and cut down sure as eggs, but perhaps we'll take a few of 'em with us.

SQUIRE TRELAWNEY: As I was saying, I'll go.

CAPTAIN SMOLLETT: Aye, you and the Doctor—take the lad, and make a run for it.

DR. LIVESEY: Shouldn't I stay and stitch up your leg?

CAPTAIN SMOLLETT: How clean are your hands?

(Livesy spits on them, wipes them off on his pants.)

DR. LIVESEY: Fair to middling.

CAPTAIN SMOLLETT: *(Declining the doctor's help:)* I'll take my chances.

DR. LIVESEY: As you wish.

SQUIRE TRELAWNEY: Quickly—before the pirates come back and kill them.

CAPTAIN SMOLLETT: Good luck, Squire.

SQUIRE TRELAWNEY: Aye. Any time. Let's go.

DR. LIVESEY: Our thoughts will be with you—

SQUIRE TRELAWNEY: Going!

(Trelawney exits out the door. The doctor and Jim follow. A beat.)

BOSUN GRAY: You said it, Cap'n. A ticklish business.

CAPTAIN SMOLLETT: This doesn't tickle, Bosun.

BOSUN GRAY: Well, no sir, I just meant...*(Beat.)* You just have no sense of humor, do you?

CAPTAIN SMOLLETT: Never saw the point to one, Bosun.

BOSUN GRAY: Fair enough.

(Lights out.)

SCENE 2

(A dark and overgrown part of the Island. Squire Trelawney, Dr. Livesy and Jim enter, single file, creeping through the jungle. Behind Jim is JEN GUNN, following in step with the others. She is dressed in rags, wearing a necklace of dead rats. They do not see her.)

SQUIRE TRELAWNEY: According to the map, it was uphill all the way to the top... Shh!

DR. LIVESEY: Shh!

JIM: Shh!

JEN GUNN: Shh!

SQUIRE TRELAWNEY: D'you get the feeling we're being watched?

DR. LIVESEY: The island is supposed to be uninhabited.

SQUIRE TRELAWNEY: Supposed to be.

JEN GUNN: It is uninhabited.

(They react.)

I should know, I've been here three years, never seen another bleedin' soul! Hee hee!

DR. LIVESEY: Who are you?

SQUIRE TRELAWNEY: *What* are you?

JEN GUNN: The queen of the island, that's me! Lived here alone, all alone for three long years. Wouldn't have a little bite of cheese about you, would you?

DR. LIVESEY: Do you always greet strangers like that?

JEN GUNN: You missed the bit where I said I was all alone on this forsaken isle?

DR. LIVESEY: Just seems a bizarre greeting, is all. Just mentioning.

JIM: But how did you get here, ma'am?

JEN GUNN: Me shipmates! Me cruel shipmates—first they doused me with brown paint!

JIM: Brown paint?

JEN GUNN: Then they covered me with red paint!

JIM: Red paint?

JEN GUNN: And then I was...MAROONED! Hee hee hee. *(Beat.)* I spent three years working on that joke.

DR. LIVESEY: Couple more and you might make it funny.

JEN GUNN: Wouldn't have any cheese on you would you? Three years I've been on this island, eating rats, no one for company but rats and more rats...pining for a little taste of home. Just a bit of cheddar to cut the taste of rat, is that too much to ask for?

SQUIRE TRELAWNEY: We don't have any cheese. What's your name?

JEN GUNN: Oh...uh....not...not sure. Around here they mostly calls me squeak squeak SQUEEE-Splat. Crunch crunch crunch.

SQUIRE TRELAWNEY: She's a mad woman. Quick, throw a rock at her.

JIM: That seems cruel.

SQUIRE TRELAWNEY: Only thing to do with mad people, Jim me boy. Ain't that right, Doctor?

DR. LIVESEY: Well, modern medicine seems to be in favor of a more humane treatment involving hitting them with sticks.

SQUIRE TRELAWNEY: Jim lad—fetch us a stick. Good stout one, perhaps with a pointy end for the poking.

JEN GUNN: Don't need any doctoring, thanking ye kindly sirs—just a bit of cheese would do. I'd make it worth your while. I knows this island like the back of a rat. If you're looking for something, I might be the one to ask, eh?

SQUIRE TRELAWNEY: We're looking for Spyglass Hill.

JEN GUNN: That's not where the treasure is.

DR. LIVESEY: Treasure?!

JEN GUNN: Treasure? What treasure?

SQUIRE TRELAWNEY: No, no, no—you said treasure. You know about it?

JEN GUNN: Might do. Might be I knows something about it, aye.

JIM: I know who you are!

JEN GUNN: How would you know that? I don't even know who I am!

JIM: You're Jennifer Gunn. You were on Flint's ship—you were the one they abandoned.

JEN GUNN: Jen Gunn. Aye, that could be it. Could be my name... How about just a bit of pepperjack? There's no cows on this island, nor goats neither. Nothing but rats, and you can't make cheese from rats.

JIM: *(To Trelawney:)* She was with Flint's crew. She knows where the treasure was buried!

JEN GUNN: It's hard enough just milking the little beggars.

(Jen mimes milking a rat. Doctor Livesy pulls Squire Trelawney aside.)

DR. LIVESEY: Squire, you've known me for many years.

SQUIRE TRELAWNEY: Aye, Doctor—I have.

DR. LIVESEY: For those many years, I've always carried a snuff box, have I not?

SQUIRE TRELAWNEY: Aye.

DR. LIVESEY: And yet, I warrant you've never seen me take so much as a dab of snuff.

SQUIRE TRELAWNEY: That's true! This entire voyage, you've remained snuffless.

DR. LIVESEY: For in truth, I do not keep snuff in my snuff box at all.

JEN GUNN: *(To Jim, but in her own world:)* If you can get'em to hold fast long enough, you've still got to milk a dozen of 'em just to get a thimble full.

DR. LIVESEY: So what's in my snuff box, you might well ask?

SQUIRE TRELAWNEY: I assume a lock of your true love's hair, perhaps, kept as remembrance?

DR. LIVESEY: No, Squire.

SQUIRE TRELAWNEY: A finger?

DR. LIVESEY: What on earth—why would you go there?

SQUIRE TRELAWNEY: Not unusual. I knew a chap named Henly, lost his big toe in a game of tiddlywinks, kept it on a string around his neck. Died from gangrene—terrible tragedy.

JEN GUNN: Then I use a toothpick to churn it....

SQUIRE TRELAWNEY: We buried the chap—and only found his big toe necklace after he was in the ground, and we couldn't decide whether it was worth digging up the whole grave just for that last little piece of him...

JEN GUNN: And d'you know what it tasted of when I was done? *(Beat.)* RAT! It tastes just like bleedin' rat!

DR. LIVESEY: *(To Trelawney:)* I carry a piece of Italian Parmigiano cheese!

JEN GUNN: Cheese, did you say?

DR. LIVESEY: Aye. I carry a piece of cheese with me in my snuff box.

JIM: That's convenient.

SQUIRE TRELAWNEY: Why did your true love give you a lock of cheese?

DR. LIVESEY: No, no—I just like it.

SQUIRE TRELAWNEY: Enough to carry it around with you.

DR. LIVESEY: Yes.

SQUIRE TRELAWNEY: Just how *much* do you like it? I mean, that's a little obsessive.

DR. LIVESEY: It's perfectly normal.

SQUIRE TRELAWNEY: I mean, I may not be a medical man, but that's bordering on a compulsion. You have to have cheese with you? What do you do with it?

DR. LIVESEY: I grate it. Occasionally.

JIM: It's very convenient. I mean, you just happen to carry cheese with you.

DR. LIVESEY: It's in the book!

JIM: It may be, but it's...it doesn't make sense!

DR. LIVESEY: When you get older, lad, you'll discover a lot of things grown ups do don't make much sense.

SQUIRE TRELAWNEY: Especially if they do them with cheese. I'm serious, I'm a little worried about you right now.

JEN GUNN: You're not just teasing a poor woman who's spent three long years living on Kentucky fried rat, are you?

DR. LIVESEY: Good woman—

SQUIRE TRELAWNEY: *(Aside:)* Mad woman.

DR. LIVESEY: Mad-woman, I am prepared to give you a piece of well travelled Italian Parmigiano cheese...

JEN GUNN: God bless you, sir!

DR. LIVESEY: ...We just need to know where Captain Flint buried his treasure.

(A beat.)

JEN GUNN: Seven hundred thousand sovereigns of gold, emeralds, rubies...you want me to give that up for a snuff box full of Parmigiano?

SQUIRE TRELAWNEY: It's a very nice snuff box.

DR. LIVESEY: Actually, I was just offering the cheese. I mean, the box...I don't like to say it, but it has sentimental value...

JEN GUNN: Just seems a little pricey. I admit, I miss cheese something fierce, I do...but that's only about four ounces there...I mean, that's what—two point eight million sovereigns a pound? Just a little up-market for old cheese. Is it organic?

JIM: Surely we should help her, Doctor? Squire? She needs medical care.

SQUIRE TRELAWNEY: Fine. Fetch me a stick.

JIM: No, no! I mean—we should take her home to England with us—if we can.

SQUIRE TRELAWNEY: Take this miserable wretch on board?

JIM: We can't leave her here.

SQUIRE TRELAWNEY: Oh my boy—you have so much to learn about the world. What we have here is termed a negotiating advantage.

JIM: And we should give her an equal share in the treasure.

SQUIRE TRELAWNEY: Hold on one moment!

JEN GUNN: An equal share in the treasure? You mean *my* treasure? I know where it is.

SQUIRE TRELAWNEY: So do we. We have a map. Well, we know where we can get one.

JEN GUNN: There's more to know than what's on the map...

JIM: An equal share. It's fair enough.

SQUIRE TRELAWNEY: While we're at it, why don't we just cut it up like a pizza? *(Beat.)* Fine. The treasure in exchange for a ride to England, passage permitting, an equal share in the treasure on safe arrival dockside, and a snuff box of cheese.

DR. LIVESEY: Without the box.

SQUIRE TRELAWNEY: A quantity of cheese approximately that contained in a regulation size snuff box.

JEN GUNN: Is there a warranty?

SQUIRE TRELAWNEY: No. It's As is.

(A beat.)

JEN GUNN: Can I see the cheese?

(Dr. Livesy, reluctantly, pulls out his snuff box and opens it. As Jen Gunn reaches for it, he snaps the box shut a la Pretty Woman*—perhaps Jen giggles in a Julia Roberts way, if the audience will be of an age to get the reference. If not, forget it. I mean, it was ages ago. Let it go, it wasn't that good a movie anyway. Where was I? Oh yes,* Treasure Island.*)*

It's very nice cheese.

DR. LIVESEY: The finest.

JEN GUNN: Awl right—ye've got yerself a deal.

(Jen spits on her hand and offers it.)

SQUIRE TRELAWNEY: Ew!

JEN GUNN: Traditional, that is. Pirate's oath.

SQUIRE TRELAWNEY: Oh, very well.

(He takes her hand, turns it palm up and spits in it as well.)

Now lead us to the treasure!

DR. LIVESEY: Wait, Squire—the lad. We know the pirates will be on their way to that exact spot, as soon as they get a party together. If it's to be an ambush—we can't take the lad into that.

JIM: I can take care of myself, Doctor.

DR. LIVESEY: I promised your mother you wouldn't do that.

JEN GUNN: The pirates are on their way? Which pirates?

SQUIRE TRELAWNEY: A one-legged woman and her ragged crew.

JEN GUNN: Long Joan Silver, by the powers! You can have yer cheese back!

SQUIRE TRELAWNEY: It's too late for that, we've spit on it. Where will the boy be safe?

JEN GUNN: Head down to Kidd's Anchorage—at the south point is a white rock. I keep a little boat there, I do—made it meself out of rat skins sewn together. Four hundred and eighty two of 'em, and pretty 'orrible work it was too. Get in the boat—and if any sees you, just paddle off, keep out of musket range. Best I can offer.

JIM: I can handle a pistol, Squire—you'll need all the hands you can get.

DR. LIVESEY: This'll be no place for a child. Now run along and paddle around in a rat skin boat trying to stay out of musket range where it's safe.

JEN GUNN: This way genn'lemen.

(They exit.)

JIM: I'm not useless! *(Beat.)* I can... A boat. A small boat...I could row up to the Hispaniola, and cut the anchor line, let her drift on the tide...let her go ashore where she fancies. Let's see those buccaneers up and sail away from us without their precious ship! Ha!

(He runs off they way they came. Lights out.)

SCENE 3

(On the Hispaniola. The Jolly Roger flies from the mast. Israel Hands stands on the railing, staring out at the island, her back to us. Mary Reade enters.)

MARY READE: They won't be back yet. Takes time to dig up a fortune in gold. Eight fortunes.

ISRAEL HANDS: Thought I saw a boat. A small boat.

MARY READE: Filled with treasure?

(Israel shakes her head.)

Eight fortunes for eight of us left. Jacquotte, Tess and Maria, cut down at the stockade. Left to rot in the sun.

(Mary takes out her pistol...considers, puts it back, and withdraws a dagger.)

ISRAEL HANDS: Aye, and a pity it is. Still, them's that fall leaves more loot for them's that are left, that's my take on it.

MARY READE: I thought that'd be yer position. You're a cold one, Israel.

(Mary steps in to stab Israel in the back...but as she does, Israel turns and stabs Mary with a knife she had ready.)

ISRAEL HANDS: I knows you, Mary. I knows you like I know me own heart.

(Israel twists the knife. Mary drops to her knees...pulls her pistol with her left hand. Israel grabs the pistol, but as she does, Mary stabs her. Israel drops the pistol, staggers back, slumps against the railing. Mary falls. A moment. As Mary dies:)

We'll ride in carriages, you said. You and me, girl. A fine carriage, horses wi' plumes on their heads, and a footman, ever so handsome, who bows when we step aboard. You and me was to be ladies, you said. Mary...I believe you've killed me.

(Israel sinks to the deck.)

So ye can't hold it against me as I returned the favor...Mary? *(Beat.)* Mary?

(Jim enters, climbing over the railing.)

Jim? Jim Hawkins?

JIM: Aye.

ISRAEL HANDS: We'm drifting.

JIM: I cut the anchor line... Then I noticed no one about, the sails untended. The ship looked derelict...plus...that boat. *(He shudders:)* That little furry boat. *(Beat.)* They still had their tails on.

(He shudders again.)

ISRAEL HANDS: Derelict...that be the word. They all went ashore, after the treasure. All but Mary, and meself.

(Jim approaches Mary's body—and picks up her pistol. He stuffs it in his belt.)

We had a falling out, as you might say, as happens with shipmates sometimes. 'Specially when one of 'em turns into a foul she-devil when she drinks.

JIM: She was drinking?

ISRAEL HANDS: No, I was.

(She tries to move – hisses in pain.)

JIM: Pain?

ISRAEL HANDS: Got plenty, thank ye. More than I care for.

JIM: I've come aboard to take possession of the ship and return to her rightful owners, Mistress Hands. You'll please regard me as your captain until further notice. First thing is to strike these colors.

(Jim hauls down the Jolly Roger and throws it overboard.)

God save the King! And there's an end to Captain Silver!

ISRAEL HANDS: Very pretty sentiments, I'll give ye—*(Referring to Mary Reade:)* ...but she's dead, and who's to sail this ship, I don't see. You? Now, look here, you gives me an old scarf or ankecher to tie my wound up, and I'll tell you how to sail her, and that's about square all round.

JIM: I'm not going back to Captain Kidd's Anchorage. I mean to get into North Inlet and beach her.

ISRAEL HANDS: To be sure you will. I've tried my fling, I have, and I've lost, and it's you has the wind of me. North Inlet? Why, I haven't no ch'ice, not I! I'd help you sail her up to Execution Dock, by thunder! So I would.

JIM: What first?

ISRAEL HANDS: Sheet the jib, we'll get her moving—but first, lad—first...get me some rum. It'll likely be me last, lad, for I'm mortal wounded, and no mistake.

JIM: If that's true, perhaps you should pray rather than drink.

ISRAEL HANDS: Pray? What fer?

JIM: What for?! You've broken your trust; you've lived in sin and lies and blood; there's a woman you killed lying at your feet this moment, and you ask me why! For God's mercy, Mistress Hands, that's why!

ISRAEL HANDS: For 30 years, I've sailed the seas—seen good and bad, fair weather and foul, starvation, no water, sailors turning on each other like dogs in the sun. I never seen good come o' goodness yet. Them as strikes first takes it is my fancy; dead men don't bite—them's my views... Amen.

(Israel suddenly lunges up – swiping at Jim with her dagger.)

JIM: Back off!

(Israel staggers forwards as Jim backs away...then he turns, and starts climbing the rigging. Israel puts the dagger in her teeth and starts after him – slowly, inching her wounded frame after him, rope by rope. Jim pulls his pistol and aims it:)

Don't come another step, Israel Hands! *(Beat.)* Dead men don't bite. Nor women neither.

ISRAEL HANDS: I reckon we're fouled, you and me...I don't have no luck, not I. One of us will have to strike.

(She takes the dagger – throws it at Jim. He fires – and she falls dead. A long moment. Jim weeps. Slowly, lights out.)

SCENE 4

(Another part of the Island. There is a mound of dirt and an old, worn shovel. Trelawney, Livesy and Gunn enter.)

JEN GUNN: That be it, genn'lemen. That's where Captain Flint herself buried her treasure.

SQUIRE TRELAWNEY: *Her*self?

JEN GUNN: Aye.

SQUIRE TRELAWNEY: I think you have been misinformed, Mistress Gunn—read the accounts.

JEN GUNN: I wouldn't know no accounts, not if they was to walk up to me and innerduce themselves, I wouldn't.

SQUIRE TRELAWNEY: Are you illiterate?

JEN GUNN: Never knew my parents.

SQUIRE TRELAWNEY: Can you read?

JEN GUNN: Where I come from, girls don't get much letterin' and such.

SQUIRE TRELAWNEY: Well, I can. I have read of the many exploits of the notorious Captain Flint—and no mention of him being one of the weaker sex.

JEN GUNN: I wouldn't call her that, having sailed with her—but she was a woman.

SQUIRE TRELAWNEY: When we get back to England, I'll show you. It's in writing.

DR. LIVESEY: That's all by the by—we're too late, dash it! The treasure is gone.

JEN GUNN: Is it now?

DR. LIVESEY: There's a dashed great hole there!

JEN GUNN: Oh, yes. So there is. Funny that.

SQUIRE TRELAWNEY: This voyage was a bad idea from the start. Didn't I say it?

DR. LIVESEY: No.

SQUIRE TRELAWNEY: Well, I must've thought it once or twice.

DR. LIVESEY: I doubt even once. *(Beat.)* Our last hope—we go to Spyglass Hill, try and sight the ship.

JEN GUNN: You don't have a knowing of where yer own ship be?

DR. LIVESEY: There's a lot going on!

JEN GUNN: You promised me England and home, you did!

SQUIRE TRELAWNEY: We agreed "passage permitting." The pirates have the ship, and now the treasure.

JEN GUNN: You don't know nothing right, do you?

SQUIRE TRELAWNEY: We find the ship...the boy had the right of it. To Spyglass Hill!

JEN GUNN: Passage permitting...I was better off with the rats.

(Lights out.)

SCENE 5

(In the Stockade – now in the dark of night, barely lit. Figures sleep on the floor. Jim enters, blue moonlight illuminating him in the doorway.)

JIM: Captain? Squire? I'm back.

THE PARROT: Pieces of Eight! Pieces of Eight!

(A lantern is lit – illuminating the pirate crew – what's left of them. The parrot perches in one of the gun portals.)

LONG JOAN SILVER: Here's Jim Hawkins, shiver me timbers! Dropped in, like, eh? Well, come, I take that friendly. Ladies, bring yourselves to! I see'd you were smart when first I set my eyes on you, but this here gets away from me clean, it do.

(Jim is speechless.)

I always liked you, I did, for a lad of spirit. I wanted you to join up and take your share, and die a gentleman of fortune, and now here ye be. Come to join us, have ye? If you like the service, a'course, well, you'm be welcome to it; and if you don't, Jim, why, you're free to answer no – free and welcome, shipmate!

JIM: Am I to answer, then?

LONG JOAN SILVER: No one's a-pressing of you. Take your bearings. None of us won't hurry you, mate; time goes so pleasant in your company, you see.

JIM: If I'm to choose, I have a right to know what's what, and why you're here, and where my friends are.

ANNE BONNEY: Wot's wot? They'd be a lucky one as knowed that!

LONG JOAN SILVER: Batten down your hatches till you're spoke to, Anne. *(To Jim:)* We got to the treasure site, all layed out in the chart—and it were gone. Someone 'ad beat us to it, and when we got back to th'anchorage, by thunder, the 'ole ship was gone! I never seen a pack o' fools look fishier; and you may lay to that. *(Beat.)* We come 'ere, and bargained wi' Captain Smollett, him and I—let'em live, we did—for the stores, brandy, the block house—a roof over our heads, for we might be heres a while. As for them, they've tramped; I don't know where. *(Beat.)* And lest you should take it into that head of yours that you was included in the treaty, here's the last word that was said: "How many are you," says I, "to leave?" "Four," says he; "four, and one of us wounded. As for that boy, I don't know where he is, confound him, nor I don't much care." Those was his words. The Doctor himself is turned against you—"ungrateful scamp" was what he said. You can't go back to your own lot, for they won't have you; and without you start a third ship's company all by yourself, which might be lonely, you'll have to join with Cap'n Silver. *(Beat.)* Now choose.

JIM: *(To all of them:)* I am not such a fool but I know what will happen in your company. I've seen too many die already. But there's a thing or two I have to tell you first. You're in a bad way—ship lost, treasure lost, crew lost, your whole business gone to wreck; and if you want to know who did it—it was I! I was in the apple barrel the night we sighted land, and I heard you, Joan, and you, Anne Bonney, and Hands, who is now dead and gone, and I told every word you said before the hour was out. As for the schooner, it was I who cut her cable, it was I that killed Israel Hands aboard of her, and it was I who brought her where you'll never see her more, not one of you. Kill me if you will, for it's all you know. I will not join you. *(Pause.)* When they kill me, Joan Silver—I'll take it kind of you to let the doctor know the way I took it.

(A moment.)

LONG JOAN SILVER: I said I'd make ye a man, Jim—but damme if ye didn't go and do it behind my back when I were watching elsewhere.

ANNE BONNEY: Killed Israel, did he? Then here goes!

(Anne leaps up, putting a dagger to Jim's throat.)

LONG JOAN SILVER: Avast, there! Anne, maybe you thought you was cap'n here, but by the powers I'll teach you better! Belay yer dirk, or you'll go where many has gone before you.

ANNE BONNEY: I stood hazing long enough, I'll be hanged if I'll be hazed by you, Silver.

LONG JOAN SILVER: I'm cap'n here, by fair election! I like that boy, now; I never seen a better boy than that. He's more a'worth than any pair of you, and I say this: let me see her that'll lay a hand on him!

CRICKET: This crew don't vally bullying a marlin-spike, and this v'yage ain't turned right no how.

MISS BEAN: Ain't turned right? Mistress Silver—I had fair employment. You promised me pockets full of gold you did. You've brought me ruin. Starvation on this island or a trip to the gallows.

LONG JOAN SILVER: Aye, them'll be by the manner of occupational hazards, and come part and parcel with 'aving yer own free choices to make, says I.

MISS BEAN: I would not have chosen this, had I but known the choice I made.

LONG JOAN SILVER: Perhaps you should've asked the Squire to choose for you, him being your lord and master.

CRICKET: Acknowledging you for to be captain at this present; but I claim my right, and ask all to step outside for a council.

(The other pirates ad lib agreement.)

ANNE BONNEY: According to rules.

LIZ PATRICKSON: Fo'cstle council. And a vote.

THE PARROT: *(Squawk:)* ...I vote for the parrot!

(The parrot exits through the gun portal. The pirates exit, leaving Silver and Jim alone.)

LONG JOAN SILVER: Jim—you're within half a plank of death, and it won't be quick nor easy. They're going to throw me off. But, you mark, I'll stand by you through thick and thin. I didn't mean to—no, not till you spoke up. I was about desperate to lose the gold and be hanged into the bargain. But I see you now, Jim Hawkins. You're the right sort. *(Beat.)* I says to myself, you stand by Hawkins, Silver, and Hawkins'll stand by you. You're his last card, and by the living thunder, he's yours! Back to back, says I. You save your witness, and he'll save your neck!

JIM: You mean all's lost?

LONG JOAN SILVER: Ship gone, neck gone—that's the size of it. Once I looked into that bay, Jim Hawkins, and seen no schooner—well, I'm tough, but I pee'd meself, just a little. I'll save your life—if I can—from that lot out there. But, see here, Jim—all square and above board—you save Long Joan from swinging at Execution Dock.

JIM: What I can do, that I'll do.

LONG JOAN SILVER: It's a bargain! I'm on the Squire's side now. I know you've got that ship safe somewheres. How you done it, I don't know, but safe it is. I know when a game's up, I do; and I know a lad that's staunch. For luck.

(She leans in – he thinks for a kiss...but she gives him a cutlass, which he conceals.)

You and me might have done a power of good together.

(The pirates enter, the Parrot returns to its portal.)

THE PARROT: Discrimination! Recount!

LONG JOAN SILVER: Step up, ladies and hand it over. I know the rules, I do; I won't hurt a deputation.

(Cricket hands over a small piece of paper with a black circle on it.)

The black spot! I thought so. Where might you have got paper?

(She turns it over:)

Property of the Gideons! You've gone and cut this out of a Bible. What fool's cut a Bible?

CRICKET: I did.

LONG JOAN SILVER: Well, you've about fixed it now among you, you'll all swing now, I reckon. What soft-headed lubber had a Bible?

ANNE BONNEY: 'twas Liz.

LONG JOAN SILVER: Elizabeth, was it? Then Liz can get to her prayers, for she's seen the end of her luck.

LIZ PATRICKSON: I knew it.

ANNE BONNEY: Belay that talk, Silver. This crew has tipped you the black spot in full council, as in dooty bound.

THE PARROT: 'Tis the black spot! Curses!

CRICKET: Aye—you'm be deposed.

LONG JOAN SILVER: Deposed, says you? By a black spot cut from a Bible? Your black spot ain't worth a biscuit. Was it I, made a hash o' this cruise? You know what I wanted! If that had been done we'd 'a been aboard the Hispaniola, the treasure in the hold, every one of us alive and loungin' on the top deck sippin' mai-tais wi' little umbrellas in'em! Well, who crossed me? Who forced my hand, as was the lawful cap'n? We're that near the gibbet that my neck's stiff with thinking on it. Kill the boy? Shiver me timbers, he's me last chance. *(To Jim:)* Here, Jim—to remember me by.

(She tosses him the black spot—and as she does, she draws her cutlass and attacks. In a trice, Jim is with her, fighting side by side. The other pirates fight back, galliantly...a furious sword fight, ranging back and forth across the blockhouse. Miss Bean is cut down by Silver's blade, Cricket killed by Jim...at one point Jim is on the ground, about to be killed but Silver saves him—at the cost of Anne's life. Eventually every pirate has fallen, only Jim and Silver left alive. The parrot is gone.)

Where be the ship, Jim, lad?

JIM: Let's find the Squire and the others first.

LONG JOAN SILVER: *(Laughing:)* Aye...when my back was turned.

(They exit. Lights out.)

SCENE 6

(On the Island Shore—bright sunlight. Livesy, Trelawney, Gray and Smollett stack supplies. Silver enters.)

DR. LIVESEY: *(Pulling a pistol:)* Stand back, Silver, or I'll take your head clean off, I will!

LONG JOAN SILVER: Don't shoot, sir! I brought you back your young man.

(Jim enters.)

DR. LIVESEY: Jim—you're safe!

CAPTAIN SMOLLETT: And in the company of a pirate.

LONG JOAN SILVER: No longer, please ye. I've come back to do me dooty, sir.

CAPTAIN SMOLLETT: Ah.

JIM: She saved my life, sirs.

CAPTAIN SMOLLETT: Did she now?

JIM: I gave my word I would speak on her account. And I will, too.

SQUIRE TRELAWNEY: Silver, you're a prodigious villain and imposter—a monstrous imposter, madam. The boy may speak for you, but the dead on this voyage hang about your neck like an albatross. You'll come back wi'us, in irons, and with a watch on you day and night. I'll not cheat the hangman, and you may lay to that, *says you.* So if you entertained notions of betraying us again, I suggest you correct yourself right quick.

LONG JOAN SILVER: Hadn't begun to even consider contemplatin' on such a circumstance, Squire.

(Jen Gunn enters, dragging a sea chest.)

JEN GUNN: Silver! Long Joan Silver!

LONG JOAN SILVER: Jennifer Gunn?!

SQUIRE TRELAWNEY: What have you there?

JEN GUNN: Oh, the treasure.

SQUIRE TRELAWNEY: The what?

JEN GUNN: Flint's treasure. Spanish gold, British silver, rubies from Abyssinia, diamonds from the far Indies, and a tennis bracelet from Tiffany's.

SQUIRE TRELAWNEY: But the buccaneers beat us to it!

LONG JOAN SILVER: The buccaneers did? That hole were dug up when we got there!

JEN GUNN: I've been here three years, you think I didn't dig up the treasure? It was in me cave the whole time. That and a hammock what I wove myself out of rat tails. Little wiggly rat tails tied in knots. *(To Jim:)* Pink ones.

(Jim shudders.)

SQUIRE TRELAWNEY: We have the treasure!

JEN GUNN: As was agreed, and spat upon. Equal shares, and a passage to England.

SQUIRE TRELAWNEY: As ever it was said so. Bosun—help Silver put that treasure in the longboat, take it to the Hispaniola, then come back and for us and the stores.

BOSUN GRAY: Leaving Silver alone in the schooner, wi' the treasure?

SQUIRE TRELAWNEY: New idea—we'll go to the boat, leaving Silver here with the treasure—no hold, stay a while... We'll keep the treasure here with us, while Silver takes our only boat—no...

LONG JOAN SILVER: Perhaps, if I may, Squire. I understand your lack of trust, I do and don't hold it against ye—my having earned it through gross dereliction of dooty, so what I says to you is—take the treasure. Ye go in the longboat, says I, as many trips as it takes, and I'll take Jen Gunn's handy little ratskin vessel, what I saw floatin' so pretty, just 'round the point. And I'll bring along a barrel or two of the salt pork and hardtack, says you, so's to save you a trip.

DR. LIVESEY: A capital idea.

LONG JOAN SILVER: By your leave, sirs. Jennifer. *(She touches her hat to Jim:)* Mister Hawkins.

(She picks up a couple of barrels, and starts to leave, then turns to Jim:)

I were born lame. When I were just a tiny thing, me mam paid a farthing for a doctor to break me leg and re-set it, so's I wouldn't grow up a beggar, ye understand. It didn't take. Me blood poisoned, and they took it off. I never had a leg, not as I can remember.

(She exits.)

SQUIRE TRELAWNEY: What a peculiar thing to say.

CAPTAIN SMOLLETT: Quite. Well—I can still row. The doctor and the bosun can best get that chest aboard at the far end.

SQUIRE TRELAWNEY: No argument—it's too hot to be lifting heavy chests, by a dashed sight.

(Livesy, Smollett and Gray pick up the treasure chest and exit.)

Why is Long Joan Silver going the wrong direction? The Hispaniola's over there.

JEN GUNN: Is she now? Not like Silver to mistake her bearings.

(A beat.)

JIM: She's not coming back, is she.

JEN GUNN: You've seen the last of her.

SQUIRE TRELAWNEY: Well, good riddance to a bad apple, I say. We've got the treasure we worked so hard for, so all's well at the last.

JIM: Flint's treasure. Thirteen dead just from our ship to get it—how many died to scrape it together? Good ships sunk and brave men drowned. What shot of cannon, what shame and lies and cruelty...Jen Gunn was there, she was one of them through it all—and there she stands, hoping nothing more than to share in its reward.

SQUIRE TRELAWNEY: You're right, Jim—we shouldn't give her any.

JEN GUNN: Then you shouldn't have spit on it! You knew who I was when you made yer deal.

JIM: That's not what I meant at all!

SQUIRE TRELAWNEY: I know what you meant, lad. But you'll find, young Jim, that there are two measures of a man. Only two. What he will die for...and what he will kill for. You made your choice aboard the Hispaniola...or did Israel Hands fall dead from a sudden attack of conscience? *(Beat.)* Aye, amazing what we could see from Spyglass Hill...we saw it all. Shot a woman dead, you did, and there's a measure for you. *(Pause.)* Here comes the Captain, back with the long boat. Climb aboard, Jim. We sail back to Bristol as rich men.

(Squire Trelawney starts off. Jim stands there, grieved...Just before Trelawney exits:)

JIM: What about what he lives for, Squire? Isn't that the true measure of a man, what he lives for?

SQUIRE TRELAWNEY: Into the boat, Jim.

(The Squire exits.)

JEN GUNN: Quick, Master Jim—into the boat. You don't want to get left behind, do you now? Takes it from old Jen Gunn, who knows this island better than anyone—it sucks. I mean, this place is an 'orrible, festerin' hole I wouldn't wish on me worst enemy, I wouldn't. Quick sir—we sail for Bristol and sweet home... And I'm goin' ta buy me a mountain of cheese!

JIM: I have no doubt you will, Jen Gunn.

JEN GUNN: And you, sir?

(A pause.)

JIM: A ship. A fair ship, well founded.

JEN GUNN: You're going after her?

JIM: Silver? In a manner of speaking.

JEN GUNN: She quite took your heart, didn't she?

(Jim looks out to sea. Very faintly, in the distance:)

THE PARROT: Pieces of eight! Pieces of eight!

(The sound fades completely.)

JIM: In a manner of speaking, Jen. In a manner of speaking.

(They exit. Lights out. End of play.)

APPENDIX—THE SEA SHANTIES

For his original novel, Robert Louis Stevenson invented a fragment of a sea shanty—only six lines, with the refrain "yo ho ho and a bottle of rum" which has become almost more famous than the rest of the book...but that fragment was based on a phrase Stevenson heard from a common stevedore's work song: "Yo heave ho." Then, in 1901, the poet Young Ewing Allison wrote "Derelict—Cap'n Billy Bones his Song," expanding on Stevenson's lyrics to create a full length version for a musical of *Treasure Island.*

In this play, I have chosen to modify Allison's words slightly, to go back to the original phrase as the second line. This isn't true to Allison's work—but it's true to Cap'n Sally Bones' character: she may have muddled the verses slightly, but she's drunk. She sings "Yo heave ho" because she's used to singing it on the deck of a working ship. Throw the emphasis on the word "heave," the way a work crew would trying to haul on a rope in unison and it feels more like a true work song.

By the way, if you want to know how you get fifteen men on one, a "Dead Man's Chest" is an island that's just a spit of sand uncovered only at low tide. It peeks above the water the way the torso of a floating corpse does, apparently. There are several small islands with the name "Dead Man's Chest," and a surprising amount of internet forum time has been wasted arguing which one Stevenson might have meant.

DERELICT – CAP'N BILLY BONES' SONG

Original Lyrics by Young E. Allison and Robert Louis Stevenson

1. Fifteen men on the Dead Man's Chest
Yo-ho-ho and a bottle of rum!
Drink and the devil had done for the rest
Yo-ho-ho and a bottle of rum!
The mate was fixed by the bos'n's pike,
The bos'n brained with a marlinspike
And Cookey's throat was marked belike,
It had been gripped by fingers ten;
And there they lay, all good dead men,
Like break-o'-day in a boozing-ken
Yo-ho-ho and a bottle of rum!

2. Fifteen men of the whole ship's list
Yo-ho-ho and a bottle of rum!
Dead and be damned and the rest gone whist!
Yo-ho-ho and a bottle of rum!
The skipper lay with his nob in gore
Where the scullion's axe his cheek had shore
And the scullion he was stabbed times four.
And there they lay, And the soggy skies
Dripped all day long in upstaring eyes-
In murk sunset and at foul sunrise-
Yo-ho-ho and a bottle of rum!

3. Fifteen men of 'em stiff and stark
Yo-ho-ho and a bottle of rum!
Ten of the crew had the Murder mark
Yo-ho-ho and a bottle of rum!
'Twas a cutlass swipe, or an ounce of lead,
Or a yawing hole in a battered head
And the scuppers glut with a rotting red,
And there they lay, Aye, damn my eyes
All lookouts clapped on paradise
All souls bound just contrariwise
Yo-ho-ho and a bottle of rum.

4. Fifteen men of 'em good and true
Yo-ho-ho and a bottle of rum!
Every man jack could ha' sailed with Old Pew
Yo-ho-ho and a bottle of rum!
There was chest on chest full of Spanish gold,
With a ton of plate in the middle hold,
And the cabins riot of stuff untold,
And they lay there, that had took the plum,
With sightless glare, And their lips struck dumb,
While we shared all by the rule of thumb
Yo-ho-ho and a bottle of rum!

5. More was seen through the sternlight screen
Yo-ho-ho and a bottle of rum!
Chartings ondoubt where a woman had been!
Yo-ho-ho and a bottle of rum!
A flimsy shift on a bunker cot,
With a thin dirk slot through the bosom spot
And the lace stiff-dry in a purplish blot.
Or was she wench, Or some shuddering maid?
That dared the knife and took the blade!
By God! she was stuff for a plucky jade
Yo-ho-ho and a bottle of rum!

6. Fifteen men on the Dead Man's Chest
Yo-ho-ho and a bottle of rum!
Drink and the devil had done for the rest
Yo-ho-ho and a bottle of rum!
We wrapped 'em all in a mains'l tight
With twice ten turns of a hawser's bight
And we heaved 'em over and out of sight
With a yo-heave-ho! And a fare-you-well!
And a sullen plunge in the sullen swell,
Ten fathoms deep on the road to hell!
Yo-ho-ho and a bottle of rum!

Derelict

As Sung by Cap'n Sally Bones

Original Tune and Lyrics by
Young E. Allison
and Robert Louis Stevenson
Modified for the play by Arthur M. Jolly

AN ACRE OF SAIL

This original sea shanty is about "Rounding the Horn"—the perilous East to West passage around Cape Horn and the Strait of Magellan, measured from crossing the 50th parallel on one side of the southernmost tip of South America to crossing it northbound on the other. It was a requisite for every trading ship and whaler trying to reach the Pacific prior to the construction of the Panama Canal. An acre of sail is an exaggeration—but the largest ships carried almost a half acre of sail, with a mainsail that could be a quarter acre of canvas on its own. A footlin' (footline) was the rope slung under the spars, and the sailors would stand on this single rope, lean over the wood spar, grab the heavy canvas with both hands and haul it up, which would swing their legs up behind them. This was called "dancing on the footlin'." They could be well over 100 feet above the deck as the ship rolled from one side to the other in a blowing gale, with no safety line, wearing heavy oiled canvas coats and wet leather boots. The idlers—the ship's carpenter, sailmaker and cook—were too important to risk sending aloft.

AN ACRE OF SAIL

Complete Lyrics by Arthur M. Jolly

1. We crossed the fifty with an acre of sail
Dance on the footlin's buckos
Pointed Magellan in the eye of a gale,
Haul in me buckos haul in.

2. The Captain stood aft with a glass in his hand
Dance on the footlin's buckos
The mate cried out that our v'yage be damned
Haul in me buckos haul in.
Haul in me buckos haul in

3. All crew up the ratlin's and crossin' the yards
Dance on the footlin's buckos
All hands to canvas and haul bloody hard
Haul in me buckos haul in.

4. She's yard arm under, the deck is awash
Dance on the footlin's buckos
The idlers all drowned, boys yer safer aloft
Haul in me buckos haul in.
Haul in me buckos haul in

5. We're roundin' the horn till the fifty be crossed
Dance on the footlin's buckos
Haul in the mains'l or th' ship will be lost
Haul in me buckos haul in.

6. The Cape winds blow from the arse of the world
Dance on the footlin's buckos
So haul in me boys 'til that acre be furled
Haul in me buckos haul in.
Haul in me buckos haul in.
Haul in me buckos, haul in—ho!

An Acre Of Sail

Words & Music by
Arthur M. Jolly

The Author Speaks

Was the structure of the play influenced by any other work?

This play is both a silly, funny version of Robert Louis Stevenson's classic drama *Treasure Island* and also a modern re-imagining of it; a way of dealing with modern themes of inequality and discrimination, reflected through the prism of 18th century life. The women in 1756 lived in a highly stratified society, but the issues they are facing in this play—poverty and restriction of options—are of course present for people in every age. The hero of the tale, young Jim Hawkins, may be facing a coming of age involving life or death stakes, and people who want to stick a sword in him or give him treasure; but the choices that he faces are the same ones everyone has to deal with growing up: What sort of person do I want to be? What do I choose as right and wrong versus what my parents have chosen, what the people around me believe?

Have you dealt with the same theme in other works that you have written?

In my drama ***A Gulag Mouse,*** five women trapped in a prison camp turn on each other to survive—in this play, the women are more of a team, joining together to fight a patriarchal society...but in both of them, themes of discrimination and injustice are interwoven. This is the first time, though, that I've really taken the question of social inequality and outright greed head on. This play—and the book it's based on—are driven by the efforts of people willing to kill each other for material wealth. The book talks about greed, and Jim Hawkins, the hero, sometimes questions the inequity of it all...but, partly from being a product of its time, it barely questions Squire Trelawney's motives. The book assumes that a rich noble will go adventuring after buried treasure for an exciting voyage... In modern society, I think there's more to examine there. The Squire is already rich—what motivates him? He may not be as bloodthirsty or ruthless as the pirates that set out deliberately to kill and steal...but he'll take the money without question no matter its origins; and unlike the pirates, he has no real need of it. The dual nature of Long John Silver's character has fascinated casual readers and academics for hundreds of years...in my version, I wanted to take the questions his character raises and apply them to some of the others as well. Who is the bad guy in ***Long Joan Silver***? For my money, the answer isn't nearly as simple as it is in the original book.

What do you hope to achieve with this work?
Immortality and to be slightly taller. I ask a lot from my plays.

What are the most common mistakes that occur in productions of your work?
Actors miss the meaning of punctuation. It's fairly uniform for modern playwrights, and it changes the meaning of the lines. An ellipsis (...) means an actor trails off, they stop talking. A hyphen or em-dash (-) means they are interrupted. Acting is about finding choices—but you need to start from a place of understanding what the text reveals. An ellipsis means a character has *made a choice* not to say something; a dash means a character has been *stopped* from achieving their goal of saying those words—that difference changes the character.

What inspired you to become a playwright?
My first production, at the Summer Shorts Festival at the Miami City Theatre. I saw a notice online that they were accepting ten-minute plays. I'd been writing for years, but I'd never even considered writing a play. I saw the notice and thought "Ten minutes? I could write a *ten-minute* play." I did,

it was accepted from over 850 submissions, and a couple of months later, I was watching my first ever play on stage in front of an audience of 300, sandwiched in between Paul Rudnick's ***Pride & Joy*** and Colin Mitchell's ***The Leap.*** Feeling the audience response all around me clarified what I wanted to do in my writing and in my life. I've been writing plays ever since.

How did you research the subject?

I started out having my mother read *Treasure Island* to me, a chapter a night, when I was seven years old, which is the best way to experience *Treasure Island,* and I strongly suggest aspiring playwrights see if my mother's available to read to them. Blind Pew terrified me—and rightfully so, he's a brilliantly crafted villain whose handicap only makes him more powerful. I re-read the book again some 10 years later, and I remember being outraged at the notion that the Doctor just happens to carry cheese with him—it seems such a coincidental cop-out. I'm glad I got to set my views out about that, some 40 years or so after first hearing the book. I also did a lot of research by watching the *Pirates of the Caribbean* movies, drinking rum (make it a Mai Tai wi' an umbrella in it, bo'sun), reading out-of-print sea faring memoirs (Dana's *Two Years Before the Mast* and Snow's *Log of A Sea Captain's Daughter* stand out), and, of course, dressing up as a pirate and strolling around various Pirate Festivals and Renaissance Faires up and down the west coast, sometimes performing sea shanties and telling stories. Yes, I'm one of those nerds. If you recognize me at one, say Arrgh.

Are any characters modeled after real life or historical figures?

All of the male characters are strictly from the book; the female characters are a couple of Robert Louis Stevenson's characters, but mostly actual historical female pirates. I was fairly liberal in taking from history—not all of them were even alive, let alone pirating, in the year the play occurs, but they were all women who made the remarkable choice to abandon their lives ashore and turn to piracy. My favorite has to be Anne Bonney, who disguised herself as a man, ran off to sea, and eventually fell in love with a young sailor...who turned out to be another woman, Mary Reade, in disguise herself. The two of them fought alongside Calico Jack Rackham for many years, before being captured. Anne Bonney once remarked, on hearing a former lover had been captured and hanged, "Well, if he had fought like a man, he need not have died like a dog." That's a pretty good character note right there.

Shakespeare gave advice to the players in *Hamlet*; if you could give advice to your cast what would it be?
Take your time, have fun, and give the audience permission to laugh. Let them finish before jumping in with the next line, even if you're sure that's the line that'll get a bigger laugh—comedy is about timing; and it's more often rushed than played too slowly. Find the funny...there are many, many more jokes than the ones in the text. A look, a reaction can add a whole new laugh—find those moments in rehearsal.

About the Author

Arthur M. Jolly was recognized by the Academy of Motion Picture Arts and Sciences with a Nicholl Fellowship in Screenwriting, and is the playwright of ***A Gulag Mouse*** (Finalist Woodward/Newman Drama Award, Winner Off-Broadway Competition, Joining Sword and Pen Competition), ***A Very Modern Marriage*** (Semi-Finalist Eugene O'Neill Theatre Center Playwrights Conference) ***Past Curfew*** (AOPW Fellowship winner), ***Trash*** (Semi-Finalist Eugene O'Neill

Theatre Center Playwrights Conference) and a collection of ten-minute plays ***Guilty Moments***. Other YouthPLAYS titles include ***The Christmas Princess, What the Well Dressed Girl is Wearing*** and ***How Blue is My Crocodile***. Jolly is a member of WGA, DGA, ALAP and is represented by the Brant Rose Agency.

About YouthPLAYS

YouthPLAYS (www.youthplays.com) is a publisher of award-winning professional dramatists and talented new discoveries, each with an original theatrical voice, and all dedicated to expanding the vocabulary of theatre for young actors and audiences. On our website you'll find one-act and full-length plays and musicals for teen and pre-teen (and even college) actors, as well as duets and monologues for competition. Many of our authors' works have been widely produced at high schools and middle schools, youth theatres and other TYA companies, both amateur and professional, as well as at elementary schools, camps, churches and other institutions serving young audiences and/or actors worldwide. Most are intended for performance by young people, while some are intended for adult actors performing for young audiences.

YouthPLAYS was co-founded by professional playwrights Jonathan Dorf and Ed Shockley. It began merely as an additional outlet to market their own works, which included a substantial body of award-winning published and unpublished plays and musicals. Those interested in their published plays were directed to the respective publishers' websites, and unpublished plays were made available in electronic form. But when they saw the desperate need for material for young actors and audiences—coupled with their experience that numerous quality plays for young people weren't finding a home—they made the decision to represent the work of other playwrights as well. Dozens and dozens of authors are now members of the YouthPLAYS family, with scripts available both electronically and in traditional acting editions. We continue to grow as we look for exciting and challenging plays and musicals for young actors and audiences.

About ProduceaPlay.com

Let's put up a play! Great idea! But producing a play takes time, energy and knowledge. While finding the necessary time and energy is up to you, ProduceaPlay.com is a website designed to assist you with that third element: knowledge.

Created by YouthPLAYS' co-founders, Jonathan Dorf and Ed Shockley, ProduceaPlay.com serves as a resource for producers at all levels as it addresses the many facets of production. As Dorf and Shockley speak from their years of experience (as playwrights, producers, directors and more), they are joined by a group of award-winning theatre professionals and experienced teachers from the world of academic theatre, all making their expertise available for free in the hope of helping this and future generations of producers, whether it's at the school or university level, or in community or professional theatres.

The site is organized into a series of major topics, each of which has its own page that delves into the subject in detail, offering suggestions and links for further information. For example, Publicity covers everything from Publicizing Auditions to How to Use Social Media to Posters to whether it's worth hiring a publicist. Casting details Where to Find the Actors, How to Evaluate a Resume, Callbacks and even Dealing with Problem Actors. You'll find guidance on your Production Timeline, The Theater Space, Picking a Play, Budget, Contracts, Rehearsing the Play, The Program, House Management, Backstage, and many other important subjects.

The site is constantly under construction, so visit often for the latest insights on play producing, and let it help make your play production dreams a reality.

More from YouthPLAYS

The Christmas Princess by Arthur M. Jolly

Fairy Tale. 60-80 minutes (flexible). 4-5+ males, 4-8+ females (8-25 performers possible, including a size and gender-flexible ensemble of dancers).

It's Christmas Eve—and the palace is in turmoil. The next day is not only Christmas, but the wedding day of the beautiful (but spoiled) Princess and the handsome (but dumb as a bag of rocks) Prince Valiant. The problem: the Princess doesn't want to marry a stupid prince. Desperate to find a way out of the marriage, she seeks the advice of Watt the Witch, who sends her on a quest to find three magical gifts that will allow her to escape her wedding.

The Mystic Tale of Aladdin by Randy Wyatt

Fantasy. 50-60 minutes. 9 females.

Seven princesses wait to hear which of them the Sultan has chosen for his bride. To pass the final minutes before he announces his decision, the maidens tell the tale of Aladdin, a tale each claims as her country's own. Filled with magic, adventure, intrigue and romance, this all-female version of the classic story packs a powerful message of empowering young women to fulfill their own wishes.

Sleepy Hollow by Elizabeth Doyle (music), Judy Freed (book), Owen Kalt (lyrics)

Musical Comedy. 90 minutes (may be cut down to a 60-minute version). 6+ males, 5+ females (11+ performers possible).

A scheming schoolmaster. An apprehensive heiress. A restless ghost with a penchant for decapitation. And a teenage girl who thinks demons are delightful. Nothing is as it seems in this fresh, funny adaptation of Washington Irving's classic American tale, *The Legend of Sleepy Hollow*.

Teen Mogul by Lucy Wang
Dramedy. 75-90 minutes. 5-16 males, 3-13 females (8-20 performers possible).

Tracy's life is turned upside down when her mother walks out. Her father can't cope, her brother's too young, and they're about to lose their home. But if Steve Jobs once called the president of Hewlett-Packard while he was still in high school, why can't Tracy call her favorite mogul and ask for a job? With a little push from her English teacher, Tracy leaps for the brass ring, but it's going to take some unlikely allies to help her navigate the prickly paths of success and save her family, her house and herself in this play inspired by a true story.

From Shakespeare with Love? by Jonathan Dorf
Comedy. 35-40 minutes. 2-9 males. 2-7 females (4-16 performers possible).

Four of the Bard's characters wait for an overdue flight to London. When Romeo reveals that he plans to revenge himself upon Shakespeare, who he blames for ruining his life, by killing him in a duel, it's up to the others—Titania, Viola and Antipholus—to save their creator by convincing Romeo that Shakespeare "does indeed love love." But as they recall scenes from their own plays as evidence, will it be all's well that ends well, or is Romeo headed for more tragedy?

screens by Jessica McGettrick
Dramedy. 35-45 minutes. 3 males, 7 females, 30 either (10-40 performers possible).

In ***screens***, we see the world through the eyes of a gamer, a lonely person looking for love, a music fan, a blogger, a bully's target and many others as they discover the perils and pleasures of creating an online persona that is different from their offline reality. What would you say if no one could see you behind the computer screen? Who would you become?

Boys vs. Girls: Armageddon by Adam J. Goldberg
Dramedy. 38-55 minutes. 5 males, 6-8 females, plus non-speaking roles (11-60+ performers.)

It's war! Nobody's quite sure how it started, but all the town's girls and boys have split up along strict gender lines and are determined to crush the opposition utterly. As water balloons fly and rumors of cootie-laced biological weapons circulate, it's up to best friends Terry and Samantha to break the gender barrier and avert mutual assured destruction.

Camp Rolling Hills by Adam Spiegel (music & lyrics), David Spiegel & Stacy Davidowitz (book & lyrics)
Musical. 90-110 minutes. 8+ males, 8+ females (16-50+ performers possible).

When 12-year-old Robert "Smelly" Benjamin is sent away to Camp Rolling Hills, he embarks on the greatest summer adventure of his life—making lifelong friends, breaking the rules, finding first love, and growing up a little along the way.

Children of Hooverville by Hollie Michaels
Drama. 45-55 minutes. 3 males, 10 females (with up to 7 additional non-speaking roles; 13-20 performers possible).

After 13-year-old Elsie Davis loses her family farm to the bank and her brother to the dust storms, she joins family and friends on a forced journey along Route 66 in search of a better life in California. Together they must survive unimaginable hardships and overcome theft, illness and unsympathetic authorities. But when at last they arrive in the Golden State, it may not be the promised land they had hoped for...

22782807R00068

Made in the USA
Charleston, SC
30 September 2013